Why Grassfed Is Best !

The Surprising Benefits of Grassfed Meat, Eggs, and Dairy Products

Jo Robinson

<u>Why Grassfed Is Best!</u>

By Jo Robinson

Robinson, Jo 1947-

Why Grassfed is Best!/Jo Robinson -1st   edition
Includes bibliographical references and index.
ISBN 0-9678116-0-0

128 pages

Printed in the United States of America
by Vashon Island Press

Vashon Island Press
29428 129th Ave S.W.
Vashon WA 98070
(206) 463-4156 during West Coast business hours.

Cover illustration by Bruce Burns. Photo on back cover by Mike Siegel.

 10 9 8 7 6   5 4 3 2 1

CONTENTS

⚘ Introduction
The New Grassfarms

In hundreds of family-owned farms across the country, a grassroots movement is underway. Animals are being taken out of their crowded feedlots and cramped cages and returned to their natural habitat—open pasture. From birth until market, cattle, bison, and sheep are being allowed to breathe fresh air and graze on lush grass. Chickens, turkeys, and pigs are free to feast on greens and forage for insects. As in nature, their rate of growth is determined by the quality of their food and the richness of their environment—not a pharmacopoeia of drugs.

Contrary to what you might think, these are not just organic farms—although many of them qualify for organic certification. What makes them unique is that the animals are given food that is very similar to what they would have eaten in the wild. Nothing more, nothing less. This means that grazing animals such as cattle, bison, and sheep get all their nutrients from pasture. Unlike commercial livestock, they are not supplemented with grain, animal by-products, synthetic hormones, or feed antibiotics. They eat what Nature intended for them to eat.

5

Reinventing Ranching from the Grass Up

Raising healthy, productive animals on pasture alone is a complex undertaking. The soil must be fertile, the grasses and legumes must suit the climate and the needs of the animals, and the animals' grazing habits must be carefully managed to keep the grass in an ideal state of growth. Because the quality of the pasture is the key to the success of these new enterprises, they are called "pasture-intensive" farms or "grassfarms," and many of the farmers refer to themselves as "grassfarmers" rather than ranchers.

As you will see, grassfarming is better for the animals, the farmers, and the environment. Just as important, the products from grassfed animals are much better for your health. They are lower in calories and "bad" fat, but higher in the "good" fats that help fight disease and promote optimal health.

Grassfarming is a win-win-win-win situation:

 Healthier for animals

 Healthier for farm families

 Healthier for consumers

 Healthier for the planet

6

↘ Chapter 1
Down on the Cattle Pharm

The life of beef cattle on the new grassfarms is similar to life on the open range. The animals are born in the field, and they spend their entire lives grazing on grass and legumes. They are able to survive and thrive on pasture alone because they belong to the family of "ruminants," animals with multi-compartmented stomachs that are designed to convert low-quality plant protein into a high-quality meal.

Commercial cattle live radically different lives. They, too, are allowed to graze on grass until they are from six to 18 months old, but then they are rounded up and shipped hundreds of miles to a feedlot to be "finished" for market. When the stressed animals arrive at the feedlot, they are introduced to an entirely artificial diet. Grain is the primary ingredient in their new rations because it speeds their growth and makes them fatter, creating the marbled beef that consumers have come to expect.

With economy the overriding principle, however, their feed may also contain any number of unsavory ingredients, including "tankage" (the ground up flesh, hooves, feathers, and bones of other animals), chicken or cattle manure[1] (an economical source of high-quality protein), stale pastry

7

(good for food energy), and ground cardboard (for that all important bulk). Typically, feed labels do not list these ingredients individually but lump them together under the generic term "by-product feedstuff."

To further stimulate the animals' growth, they are dosed with synthetic hormones and antibiotics. According to *Livestock and Poultry Production,* "The use of antibiotics and hormones as feed additives is one of the most effective management tools available to beef cattle producers. Combining [synthetic hormonal] implants with feed additives improves performance more than using either alone."[2] An estimated 95 percent of our feedlot cattle are now being treated with growth-promoting hormones.[3]

This biotech combination of grain, by-product feedstuff, antibiotics, and hormones achieves its goal: our feedlots produce vast quantities of marbled, USDA-approved meat at a reasonable cost.

It's Not Nice to Fool Mother Nature

But whenever we clever humans interfere with nature on a grand scale, there's a price to pay. In this case, the animals pay some of the cost. Ruminants have difficulty digesting large amounts of grain because they lack a critical enzyme needed to metabolize starch. Care must be taken to introduce the artificial diet slowly or the animals will become sick and perhaps die. Even after adapting to the feedlot diet, they continue to have food-related problems. Disorders linked with grain feeding include bloat, acidosis,[4] laminitis, liver abscesses,[5] telangiectasis, and sudden death syndrome.[6] To control these diseases, the animals are treated with yet more antibiotics and medications.

We humans pay a price as well. The 20 million pounds of antibiotics fed to our livestock each year are spawning antibiotic-resistant bacteria.[7]   Alarmingly, the percentage of salmonella resistant to five different antibiotics has increased from less than one percent in 1980 to 34 percent in 1996. Much of this increase is due to the routine use of feed antibiotics in the livestock industry.[8]   Some believe it's only a matter of time before these superbugs cause widespread health problems.[9]

Just as ominous, treating animals with synthetic hormones could be increasing our risk of cancer and other disorders. A key finding is that growth hormones increase the amount of "insulin-like growth factor-1" or IGF-1 in cow's milk. Pasteurization increases IGF-1 levels even further. A growing body of evidence incriminates IGF-1 "as a potential risk factor for both breast and gastrointestinal cancers."[10]

Another drawback to modern feedlot practices is that the grain fed to cattle is treated liberally with pesticides, and these chemicals are finding their way into our own food supply. According to the Environmental Protection Agency, 90-95% of all pesticide residues are found in meat and dairy products.

Disturbing findings such as these are fueling the fast-growing organic food industry. People want and deserve to have wholesome food that is free of antibiotics, synthetic growth hormones, and pesticide residues. But raising meat animals organically is not enough. As you will see in the next chapter, the simple act of feeding large amounts of grain to animals that evolved eating grass loads their meat with fat and calories and diminishes its nutritional value. Animals need more than an organic diet—they need their *original* diet.

9

Grassfed Beef

 ⟸ **Feed Ingredients:**
Pasture

Feedlot Beef

 ⟸ **Possible Feed ingredients:**
Chlortetracycline, bacitracin, methylene disalicylate, erythromycin, tylosin oxytetracycline, sulfamethazine, ethlenediamine dihydroiodide, lasalocid sodium, monensin, melengestrol acetate, zeronal, testosterone, estradiol benzoate, progesterone, trenbolone acetate, sodium bicarbonate, poloxaline, hydroxyzine, sodium bentonite, propionic acid, chicken manure, cattle manure, chocolate, stale pastry, cement dust, molasses, candy, urea, hooves, feathers, meat scraps, fish meal, pasta, peanut skins, brewery wastes, cardboard, corn silage, genetically modified grain, pesticides...

☙ Chapter 2
The Superiority of Grassfed Meat and Dairy Products

When ruminant animals are fed large amounts of grain, their meat and milk products are less desirable for human health. One of the most significant drawbacks is that their meat has more of the "bad" fat that clogs our arteries and less of the "good" fat that enhances our health.

Let's take a closer look at grainfed beef. When cattle have spent their requisite four to eight months in a feedlot, their meat has four to six times more total fat than meat from grassfed cattle.[11] Significantly, it has twice as much saturated fat. A diet high in saturated fat has been linked with a higher risk of cardiovascular disease and diabetes.[12] Not without reason, "Eat less red meat!" has been a rallying cry of dieticians.

New research suggests that "Eat less *grain-fed* meat" would be better advice. When cattle are allowed to remain on pasture, their meat has about the same amount of fat as wild game or a skinless chicken breast.[13] When red meat is this lean, it actually *lowers* your cholesterol levels.[14] This means that even people with high cholesterol levels can enjoy grassfed beef, bison, and lamb—with their doctors' seal of approval.

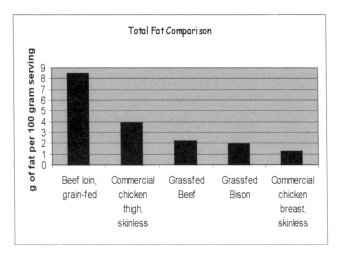

Calories Do Count

Because grassfed beef is so much leaner than grainfed meat, it is also lower in calories. (Fat has 9 calories per gram, compared with only 4 calories for protein and carbohydrates. The greater the fat content, the greater the number of calories.) A 6-ounce steak from a grass-finished steer has almost 100 fewer calories than a 6-ounce steak from a grainfed steer.[15] If you eat a typical amount of beef (66.5 pounds a year), switching to grassfed beef would save you 17,733 calories a year—without requiring an ounce of willpower. All things being equal, you would lose about six pounds a year. If all Americans switched to grassfed meat, our national epidemic of obesity would begin to diminish.

Grassfed Animals Are Richer in Omega-3s

Feeding grain to cattle changes their meat in a less obvious but equally important way: it diminishes its supply of a type of good fat called "omega-3 fatty acids." Grassfed meat has from two to six times more omega-3s than grainfed meat.[16]

The very notion of a "good fat" takes some people by surprise. But omega-3 fatty acids are not only good for your health, they are essential for normal growth and development. Furthermore, you can't manufacture them in your body, so you must get them from your diet. This is why omega-3 fatty acids are one of the few fats to be classified as "essential fatty acids."

New research, most of it conducted since 1985, reveals that every cell and system in the human body relies on omega-3s.[17] Your brain, for example, is largely composed of fat, and omega-3 fatty acids are the most important of those fats. If your diet has an adequate amount of these nutrients, you have a lower risk of a host of mental disorders including depression,[18] aggressive behavior, attention-deficit disorder (ADD), schizophrenia, and dementia.[19] Researchers are now experimenting with treating these disorders with omega-3s, with some preliminary successes.[20]

Your cardiovascular system is equally dependent on omega-3s. People with diets rich in omega-3s are less likely to have high blood pressure or irregular heart rhythms.[21] Remarkably, they are half as likely to die from a heart attack or stroke.[22]

People with an adequate supply of omega-3s may also be less vulnerable to cancer.[23] For example, a French study determined that women with the highest levels of omega-3s in their tissues were least likely to have invasive breast cancer.[24] Heart patients who followed an omega-3 rich diet for three years not only had a 70 percent reduction in the risk of dying from a heart attack, they had a 61 percent reduction in the risk of dying from all types of cancer.[25]

The disease-fighting properties of omega-3 fatty acids take on more significance when you

13

realize that the American diet is greatly deficient in these fats. Only 40 percent of Americans consume adequate levels. Twenty percent have levels so low that they defy detection.[26]

As you can see by the following graph, feeding grain to ruminants is one of the hidden reasons for this widespread deficiency. Every day that an animal spends in the feedlot, its meat contains fewer and fewer omega-3 fatty acids. By the time the meat is deemed fit for consumption, it is almost devoid of omega-3s.[27]

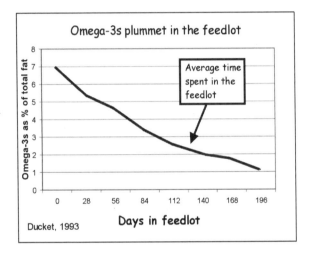

There is a simple explanation for the rapid decline in omega-3s in grain-fed cattle: omega-3s are formed in the green leaves of plants. When the animals graze on their natural diet of greens, their diet is automatically rich in these essential fats. (Sixty percent of the fat in grass is a type of omega-3 fatty acid called "alpha-linolenic acid" or LNA.) When the animals are taken off fresh pasture and fed ingredients poor in omega-3s (such as grain), their tissues gradually lose their store of these potentially lifesaving fats.

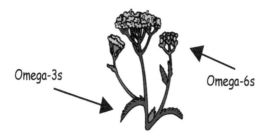

Omega-3s

Omega-6s

What's more, the animals accumulate higher than normal amounts of a competing type of essential fatty acid called "omega-6 fatty acids" which are most highly concentrated in the seeds of plants. Excessive amounts of omega-6s have been linked with a higher risk of obesity, diabetes, cancer, and immune disorders such as asthma and arthritis.[28]

A grain diet has the same detrimental effect on bison, sheep and other ruminants that it does on cattle—it makes their meat and dairy products higher in fat and disrupts their normal ratio of essential fatty acids. For decades, the term "grainfed meat" has been interpreted as an assurance of quality. In reality, it should be a warning sign that the meat is going to be less desirable for human health.

Warning: This animal
Was Grainfed !

The Graining of Bison

Due to growing consumer demand for nutritious lean meat, bison (American buffalo) are making a comeback. By the end of the 1800s, a population that had once numbered in the tens of millions had dwindled to fewer than 1,000 wily survivors. Today, bison are no longer classified as endangered. Approximately 225,000 bison are being raised for market in North America, with the numbers expected to increase 25 percent each year. Even so, demand is outstripping supply. Health-conscious consumers like the fact that bison meat is higher in protein than beef, but lower in fat, cholesterol, and calories. Although the nutritional profile of bison resembles wild game, it has a mild, almost sweet flavor more reminiscent of beef than elk or venison.

What many people do not realize, however, is that most of these magnificent animals are now being rounded up and shipped to the feedlot, just like cattle. And, just like cattle, a feedlot diet diminishes the nutritional value of their meat. The following graph shows the marked difference in the omega-3 content of grassfed and grainfed bison.[29]

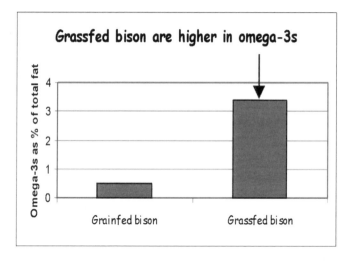

Feeding grain to bison makes even less sense than feeding grain to cattle because bison are such efficient grazers. For example, bison put on very little weight during the winter months—which is precisely when the grass goes dormant. When the grass rebounds in the spring, the animals can put on weight very quickly, a phenomenon known as "compensatory gain." Thus, the physiology of the bison and the growing cycle of the prairie grasses are in perfect harmony, a synergism that is the result of millions of years of co-evolution.

This may change. A number of ranchers who fatten their bison on grain are selecting their breeding stock from those few animals that tend to put on weight year round. An animal that gains weight steadily during the winter months is more valuable to them because it reaches market size more quickly in the feedlot.

Farmers who raise their bison on grass alone reject this "bigger, faster, better" mentality. "We focus our energy on improving the pasture, not the bison," says Jan Moseley of the Texas Bison Company. "We think that the bison are pretty highly evolved just as they are." In the resource section of this book, you will find a number of other bison ranchers who share this "hands-off" philosophy.

Omega-3 Rich Dairy Products

Conjure up an image of a dairy cow, and you probably see a contented cow munching on emerald grass. In reality, most of our dairy cows stand around on concrete pads in corporate-owned confinement dairies where they are implanted with synthetic hormones, dosed with antibiotics, and fed an artificial grain diet. The reason the cows are subjected to this treatment, of course, is that it greatly increases their milk production. In the 1940s, a good milk cow produced 4500 pounds of milk per lactation. Today, our hormone-implanted super cows pump out 17,000 pounds each, almost a four-fold increase. This is 20 times more milk than a cow needs to produce to nourish a healthy calf.

In all of the euphoria over increased milk production, the dairy industry has failed to convey to the public that the milk, butter, and cheese from grainfed cows are deficient in a number of good fats, including omega-3 fatty acids.[30]

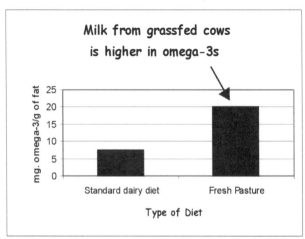

CLA-the Hidden Bonus in Grassfed Ruminants

Ruminants are the richest known source of another good fat called "conjugated linoleic acid" or CLA. CLA is found in meat and milk, but it is most highly concentrated in milk fat—the very fat we've been taught to avoid. The more fat in a given dairy product, the more CLA it contains. Nonfat dairy products have virtually no CLA. The amount of CLA in dairy products is also greatly influenced by the diet of the cows. Significantly, milk from grassfed cows contains as much as five times more CLA than milk from standard, grainfed cows.[31]

Researchers did not get their first glimpse of the many health benefits of CLA until 1987. Although the research is in its earliest stages, CLA shows promise of reducing the risk of cancer, obesity, diabetes, and a number of immune disorders. What's more, CLA appears to be perfectly safe. Even in very large doses, this good fat has shown no harmful effects in laboratory animals.[32]

CLA Fights Cancer

At this point in time, the research on CLA and cancer is the most promising. When rats are fed very small amounts of CLA—a mere 0.1 percent of their total calories—they show a significant reduction in tumor growth. At 1.5 percent of their caloric intake, tumor size is reduced by as much as 60 percent. One reason this research is so intriguing is that, to date, virtually all of the natural cancer-fighting substances have come from plants. According to Clement Ip, PhD, a lead researcher in the field, "CLA is unique because it is present in food from animal sources."[33]

It's too early to say whether CLA will help fight cancer in people as well. (A well-designed cancer prevention study costs tens of millions of dollars and takes decades to administer.) But there are hints that it might. A 1996 study of 4,697 women found that the more full fat milk in the women's diets (thus the more CLA) the lower their risk of breast cancer. The women who drank the most milk had a 60 percent lower risk.[34] Other surveys have found a link between milk consumption and a lower risk of colon cancer.[35]

Eat Fat; Get Lean

"Eating fat makes you fat" is a maxim that most people accept without question. But CLA is no ordinary fat. Amazingly, it helps convert fat to lean muscle-every dieter's dream. The fat-burning property of CLA was first noted in animal studies. In one of these experiments, mice given CLA gained only 30 percent as much body fat as a group not given the nutrient.[36] We humans may respond in a similar way. In a 3-month study, 20 inactive men and women were given either CLA supplements (3 grams a day) or placebos. Even though neither group exercised more or ate less, the CLA group lost an average of five pounds and had a significant 15 to 20 percent drop in body fat.[37] The placebo group had little or no change in weight or body fat. Larger studies are underway.

A second study tested CLA's muscle-building properties. Young men taking part in a weight-training program were given either CLA or placebos. After 28 days, the CLA group could bench-press 30 pounds more than they had at the beginning of the program. The placebo group improved their weight-lifting ability by only nine pounds.[38]

Grassfed Meat and Dairy Products
"They do a bodybuilder good!"

Synthetic CLA is available in health food stores and is being avidly purchased by body builders and dieters. But there is an important difference between synthetic CLA and the kind found in meat and dairy products: the supplements have a lower biological activity and may require more than twice the amount to achieve the same results. They are also very expensive. It makes more sense to get your CLA from meat and dairy products—as long as the animals were fed grass and not grain. To equal the amount of CLA you'd get from one slice of cheese from a grassfed cow, you would have to eat five slices of cheese from a grainfed cow. This would burden you with 452 extra calories and 37 unnecessary fat grams![40]

Bison, sheep, goats, and cattle raised exclusively on grass give you the same CLA advantage—not just in their fat but in their lean muscle as well. A preliminary analysis of grassfed beef from the River Run Farm in Clatskanie, Oregon, revealed that the meat had 4 to 5 times more CLA than conventional meat.[41]

Do Grassfed Products Have Enough CLA to Influence Your Health?

When you hear about promising dietary substances such as CLA, it's important to determine whether

the amount you would normally consume is sufficient to give you the promised results. All too
often, one has to eat unrealistic amounts of food to
gain any significant benefits. So, is there enough
CLA in grassfed products to reduce your risk of
cancer? Probably so. It has been estimated that
people eating ordinary grainfed meat and dairy
products consume about 1 gram of CLA a day.[42]
Judging by animal studies, this is one third of the
amount required to reduce the risk of cancer.
Switching to grassfed animal products would increase your CLA intake three to five times, which
could make the all-important difference. Dr. Tikal
Dhiman from Utah State University estimates that
you should be able to lower your risk of cancer
simply by eating the following foods each day: one
ounce of cheese and one glass of whole milk from a
grassfed cow, plus one serving of grassfed meat.[43]
The fact that people living a century ago would have
eaten these foods as a matter of course may help
explain our much higher rate of cancer today.

A Novel Cancer Fighting Diet

When God Holds the Patent

As you might imagine, enterprising researchers are
searching for ways to make ruminants produce even
more CLA; any natural substance that helps fight
cancer and converts fat to muscle is destined to be

a hot area of research. In one elaborate experiment, dairy cows were divided into groups and fed a variety of different diets, including fish meal, high-oil corn, and a metabolic modifier. None of these machinations proved as effective as simply turning the cows loose on fresh pasture. According to this 1999 study, "Cows grazing pasture and receiving no supplemental feed had 500% more [CLA] in milk fat than cows fed typical dairy diets."[44] Fortunately, God has the patent on both grass and cows, so no company will ever have a monopoly on grassfed dairy products!

A Closer Look at CLA

Conjugated linoleic acid or CLA is made in the rumen (stomach) of grazing animals. CLA closely resembles an omega-6 fatty acid called "linoleic acid" or LA. Both CLA and LA have 18 carbon atoms and two double bonds holding the chain together. The only difference is in the placement of those bonds. LA has double bonds between the 9th and 12th carbon atoms, and the most common form of CLA has them between the 9th and 11th.

This seemingly insignificant change—one that can be detected with only the most sophisticated instruments—dramatically alters the way the molecules function in your body. For example, LA promotes tumor growth; CLA blocks it. LA is linked with a greater risk of diabetes and obesity; CLA may lower the risk.

Researchers are beginning to understand CLA's unique fat-burning properties. Apparently, CLA blocks an enzyme called "lipoprotein lipase" that moves fat from the blood into storage in the body's fat cells. It also enhances the action of another enzyme called "hormone sensitive lipase" that breaks down the fat that is already deposited in the cells, liberating it to be used as fuel for nearby muscle cells. The net result is less fat, more fuel.

Golden Butter, Creamy Fat, Orange Yolks

In addition to giving you a bounty of omega-3 fatty acids and CLA, grassfed animals are also richer in beta-carotene, a vitamin linked with a lower risk of cancer and cardiovascular disease.[45] Grass contains more beta-carotene than grain, so as long as animals remain on fresh pasture, their meat, eggs, and dairy products are a good source of this key vitamin. Take them off pasture, and they become relatively deficient in this nutrient, even though they are fortified with synthetic vitamins.

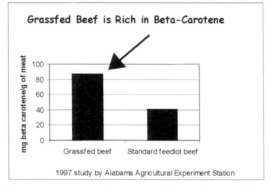

Grassfed Beef is Rich in Beta-Carotene

1997 study by Alabama Agricultural Experiment Station

Beta-carotene is naturally yellow-colored, which can give the fat of grassfed animals a creamy color. This can dismay American consumers who have grown accustomed to seeing the white, vitamin-deficient fat of feedlot cattle. In fact, according to a report issued by the University of California, "Discounts on [beef] of up to 20 cents per pound can occur due to the public's conditioned preference to the white fat produced from grain feeds that are lower in beta carotene."[46] To protect the economic value of their meat, producers go to great lengths to rid beef fat of its natural creamy color. A tried and true solution is to give animals food that is low in beta-carotene. Feeding turnips to cattle, for example, produces the coveted chalk-white fat. The fact that these artificial diets also make the meat deficient in beta-carotene, CLA, and omega-3 fatty acids is a closely guarded secret.

Raising cattle and sheep on pasture alone has remained the norm in a few countries around the world-notably Argentina, New Zealand, and Scotland. In those countries, white fat is considered less healthy, which indeed it is. An Argentinean chef once remarked, "Looking at the fat of a USDA Choice steak is like looking at the face of a dead man."

USDA Choice . . . But whose choice is it?

Grassfed Meat Lowers Your Risk of *E. coli*

There is yet one more compelling reason for switching to grassfed animal products—you will lower your risk of becoming infected with pathogenic *E. coli* bacteria.

E. coli are abundant in all ruminants (including those raised on pasture) because the bacteria are essential for their normal digestive process. During processing, it is possible for some of the bacteria from an animal's gut to contaminate its meat. If the meat is improperly handled or served undercooked, you can become infected. (You can also get *E. coli* from fruits and vegetables fertilized with manure.)

25

Luckily, most strains of *E. coli* cause only mild gastric problems, but rare strains, in particular one known as *E. coli* 0157:H7, can cause serious, even fatal illness, especially in young children and those with compromised immune systems. One of the more serious outbreaks took place in the Pacific Northwest in 1993, sickening 700 people and killing four. (The *E. coli* was traced to undercooked hamburgers served at a fast-food chain.)

A recent study found that animals fed corn silage and animal by-products are more likely to carry *E. coli* 0157:H7 than other animals, suggesting that strictly grassfed animals are less likely to harbor the pathogenic bacteria.[47]

But more important, even if grassfed meat should happen to be contaminated with a deadly strain of *E. coli*, your chances of becoming seriously ill are greatly reduced. Here's why. One of our main defenses against *E. coli* is the natural acidity of our digestive system. As long as the *E. coli* remain vulnerable to an acid environment, we are well protected. Unfortunately, feeding large amounts of grain to a ruminant increases the acidity of its digestive tract, giving the *E. coli* a chance to become acclimated to a more acid environment. When we ingest these acid-resistant bacteria, we have a much harder time destroying them.

A study published in 1999 in the journal *Science* showed that our gastric juices can destroy 99.99 percent of the normal type of *E. coli* found in grassfed animals. By contrast, a high percentage of the acid-resistant *E. coli* from grainfed animals can survive the acid bath in our stomachs and could cause major health problems.[48]

One of industry's proposed solutions to the growing incidence of *E. coli* outbreaks is to irradiate our meat. But pioneering grassfarmers offer a more "basic solution"—raise our cattle on fresh pasture so that the bacteria can be destroyed by our own natural defenses!

Don't irradiate !   Pasture-ize!

Beyond Organic

Switching from grainfed to grassfed meat and dairy products gives you a wealth of health benefits. First of all, you avoid all the synthetic hormones, antibiotics, pesticide residues, and questionable additives found in conventionally raised animals. But just as important, you get these added nutritional advantages:

- **Less fat**
- **Fewer calories**
- **More omega-3 fatty acids**
- **More CLA**
- **More beta-carotene**
- **A lower risk of E. coli**

It's important to keep in mind that all of the six benefits listed above are the direct result of raising animals on fresh pasture. Products from animals fed significant amounts of grain will not have these benefits—even when the grain has been organically grown. The grain, itself, is the problem, not the way it's been treated. Whenever ruminant animals are taken off their original diet of grass and switched to an artificial diet of grains and "by-product feedstuff," their meat and dairy products are less beneficial for our health. Keeping them on pasture helps protect our health as well as theirs.

≫ Chapter 3
The Benefits of Pastured Poultry

Ruminants are not the only animals you will find happily grazing on pasture-intensive farms. Chickens and turkeys are busily foraging as well. Unlike ruminants, however, poultry cannot survive on pasture alone. Because they lack a multi-compartmented stomach, they need some form of high quality protein, such as insects or a mixture of grains and legumes. But greens are a key part of their natural diet as well. Chickens that are raised on pasture will get as much as 30 percent of their calories from grass, clover, and other greens. Turkeys are more eager grass eaters and can glean as much as 50 percent of their calories from pasture.

One hundred years ago, all of our chickens and turkeys were "pastured poultry." Free to scavenge for greens and bugs, they provided orange-yolked eggs for breakfast and meaty roasts for Sunday supper. Granted, the old-fashioned system was not very efficient. Grandma's laying hens went through a prolonged molt every year, which cut into their egg production. The birds also laid fewer eggs in the winter, a much needed vacation that allowed them to restore the minerals that had been depleted by egg-laying. All in all, Grandma could count on only 200 eggs per chicken per year, even from her best layers.

Today, our super-efficient layers are vaccinated, medicated, debeaked, confined in cages, fed high-energy diets, and exposed to a carefully orchestrated lighting environment. The artificial lights eliminate the seasonal dip in production, and the special feeding and management techniques shorten the molt. As a result, the hens can pump out as many as 300 eggs per year.

As you might imagine, the birds pay a price for this efficiency. They have little room to move, breathe large amounts of ammonia and fecal dust, and can become literally paralyzed with "cage fatigue." Once their production declines, they may be rewarded for their efforts by being ground up and fed to other chickens as "spent hen meal."

People who work in chicken factories suffer as well. They, too, are exposed to the fumes and dust, giving them a higher rate of asthma and respiratory diseases.[49] Their accident rate is twice as high as the overall industry average due to the break-neck pace of production.[50]

People outside the poultry industry know little of these matters. All they see are the cartons of AA eggs and plastic-wrapped fryers neatly arrayed in supermarket cases.

Would You Like Your Eggs Scrambled or Medicated?

If people could scrutinize these poultry products as scientists have, they might have second thoughts about buying them. A recent finding is that the antibiotics and medications routinely given to commercial laying hens can linger in their eggs long after all traces are gone from their blood.[51] Little did you know that when you buy a dozen eggs from the supermarket you might be getting a free dose of antibiotics as well.

Worse yet, those eggs may contain antibiotic resistant bacteria. In a 1997 study, scientists isolated bacteria from chicken eggs and exposed them to a wide range of antibiotics. They detected resistant strains of Staphylococcus aureus, Entero-coccus faecalis, E. coli, Enterobacter cloacae, Pseudomonas stutzeri, and Citrobacter freundii—a veritable army of superbugs![52]

Where Are the Omega-3s?

Meanwhile, one pioneering researcher has discov-ered what supermarket eggs don't have—their full allotment of omega-3 fatty acids. Artemis P. Simopoulos, M.D., chair of the Nutrition Coordinat-ing Committee of the National Institutes of Health for nine consecutive years, became interested in the changing food value of eggs during a visit to her family's ancestral farm in Greece in the 1980s. Simopoulos observed that her parents' free-ranging hens spent much of their time foraging on wild greens, in particular a common weed called purslane. In earlier research, she had discovered that purslane is unusually high in omega-3s. She won-dered—would the nutritional content of the greens be reflected in the hens' eggs? To find out, she hard-boiled half a dozen eggs and took them back to the United States for analysis. When she com-pared the free-range eggs to supermarket eggs, she found the free-range eggs contained almost twenty times more omega-3 fatty acids! The ratio of omega-6 to omega-3 fatty acids in the eggs was similar to the ratio found in eggs from wild birds, which is an ideal one-to-one. The supermarket eggs had a top-heavy ratio of 20 to one, reflecting the high-grain, low-greens diet of factory hens.[53]

Chickens on the Fast Track

In the past 50 years, the broiler chicken industry has changed just as dramatically as the layer industry, with similar compromises in nutritional value. Today's broilers reach market size three times faster than Grandma's laid-back chickens. In 1935, a typical four-month-old chicken weighed 2.8 pounds. In 1994, two-month-old broilers tipped the scales at over four pounds![54] This greatly accelerated growth is fueled by selective breeding, high-energy feed, antibiotics, appetite stimulants, and round-the-clock artificial lighting. The fact that the chickens grow so fast that their leg bones become deformed and their hearts and lungs begin to fail has not slowed the experiments. In fact, studies are now underway to see if injecting hormones into chicken embryos before they hatch will get the birds to your table even sooner.[55]

Setting Chicken Farming Back 100 Years

Fortunately for us, grassfarmers are bucking these trends and raising their poultry outdoors on high-quality pasture. The chickens are getting their light from the sun and their vitamin supplements from the grass and bugs. This old-fashioned system is better for everyone involved—the chickens, the farmers, and the consumers.

Just how much better pastured poultry products are for your health was revealed in a recent study funded by the USDA Sustainable Agriculture and Research Education Program (SARE). An independent lab compared the nutritional value of broilers raised on pasture with conventionally raised chickens. The free-range chickens had 21 percent less total fat, 30 percent less saturated fat, and 28 percent fewer calories. The breast meat was so lean that the USDA could classify it as "fat free". Yet the meat had 50 percent more vitamin A and 100 percent more omega-3s.[56]

Meat from pastured poultry is not only healthier, it tastes better as well. In a blind taste test of ordinary and free-range Thanksgiving turkeys, *New York Times* food editors chose a free-range bird as their number one choice. The meat was flavorful and juicy, and had a tender but meaty texture. Owners of fine restaurants concur. When you order chicken or turkey at an upscale restaurant, the meat is likely to come from a free-range bird.

MegaEggs

The SARE study mentioned above also established the nutritional superiority of eggs from pastured poultry. Compared with eggs from caged birds, they had 10 percent less fat, 40 percent more vitamin A, and 400 percent more omega-3 fatty acids. An unexpected finding is that the eggs also had 34 percent less cholesterol (160 mg. per egg versus the customary 214.) The reason this finding is noteworthy is that poultry scientists have ransacked the chemistry labs for decades trying to create low-cholesterol eggs. Among other concoctions, hens have been fed such tasty tidbits as cupric sulfate pentahydrate, cholesterol O-acyltransferase, lovastatin, colestipol, and di-(2-ethylhexyl) phthalate—with little or no change in egg cholesterol levels. Now we know that letting hens loose to forage for greens and insects does the trick. Once again, nature's original plan is proving to be the superior plan.

The benefits of eating eggs rich in omega-3 fatty acids have been shown in several studies. In one such study, 23 people added either two regular eggs or two omega-3 enriched eggs to their normal diet for 18 days. Those who ate the ordinary eggs had higher cholesterol levels at the end of the study. Those who ate the omega-3 eggs, had no change in total cholesterol. Even better, their HDL or "good" cholesterol went up and their "bad" triglycerides went down, for a net benefit to the cardiovascular system.[57]

But it doesn't take a medical study to convince most people that eggs from pastured hens are superior. A grassfarmer who sells her eggs at a farmer's market reports, "All I have to do is crack open one of our eggs and an ordinary egg. One look, and people line up to buy ours. The yolks are almost orange! We have to ration the eggs to have enough for our regular customers."

Buyer Beware

When you are shopping for pastured poultry products, you need to be on the lookout for pale imitations. Eggs, chickens, and turkeys advertised as "free-range" or "organic" are now available in many stores, where they command a premium price. But neither of these designations guarantees that the birds have been raised on pasture. To qualify as "free-range," birds have to have access to the outdoors, but there is no guarantee that they will find any fresh greens. The term "organic" may be your assurance that the product will be free of pesticides, chemical fertilizers, and synthetic hormones, but it does not guarantee that the birds will have an omega-3 rich diet.

34

When shopping for poultry, you need to be wary of other terminology as well. Chickens described as "uncaged" are probably spending all their time milling around with 10,000 other birds in a crowded shed. The fact that they are not locked into individual cages may be good for their psyches, but their meat and eggs will be little different from the kind you find in the supermarket.

"Natural" is one of the most deceptive words in the food industry. Any raw meat can be described as "natural" if it has not been treated with chemicals during processing. The term has nothing to do with the way the animals were treated while alive. Under this limited definition, even factory chickens can be described as healthy and natural, as you can see by the following excerpt from the Tyson website: "The leading national brands are just as natural as free range chickens. Most commercially grown chickens are fed only the highest quality grains, vitamins and minerals, in a controlled environment, to ensure a healthy, all natural product."[58]

In the resource section of this book, you will find dozens of grassfarmers who have a more comprehensive definition of the term "all natural." They raise their poultry outdoors on fresh pasture, and they do not use antibiotics, appetite stimulants, or synthetic hormones. Some grassfarmers house their poultry in portable, bottomless cages that are moved daily; others let their chickens forage in open fields. Either system assures that the birds have adequate exercise, fresh air, and sunshine, and that their meat and eggs have their full complement of nutrients.

⇘ Chapter 4
A Diet in Synch with Our Genes

With so many advantages to eating grassfed meat, poultry, and dairy products, one senses that there must be something inherently "right" about them. Indeed, there is. When we feed animals their original diet, we are feeding them the food that is most in harmony with their genetic make-up. This more natural diet produces naturally healthy animals. The same is true for us. When we eat grassfed products, we are eating food that is ideally suited for our genetic make-up. One might say that our bodies "expect" to be fed grassfed products.

To see why this is so, consider the human evolutionary diet, the diet that sustained our species throughout our long saga of evolution. The diet varied with time and geography, but certain qualities were fairly consistent. For example, compared to our modern diet, the Paleolithic diet (the "caveman" era from 15,000 to 750,000 years ago) was low in total fat, low in saturated fat, but relatively high in omega-3 fatty acids.[59]

These differences are due, in part, to the role that wild game played in the diet. Approximately 30 percent of the calories in the "caveman" diet are believed to have come from meat. This meat was so different from our modern feedlot meat, however, that it might as well have been a totally different type of food. In the 1960s, British researcher Michael Crawford compared beef purchased at the supermarket with a similar cut from a wild Cape buffalo, a type of game animal that might have been hunted by early hunters and gatherers. He found that the buffalo meat had one tenth as much total fat, half as much saturated fat, but six times more omega-3s.[60] A diet that contained significant amounts of wild game would have had similar characteristics.

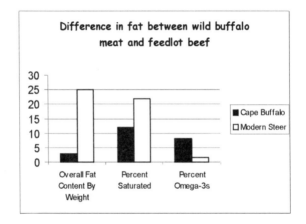

The Diet of Our Earliest Ancestors

Much less is known about the diet of the hominids who preceded the cavemen. Unfortunately, these earliest ancestors left no cave paintings, stone tools, or pottery fragments for us to scrutinize. Until the 1990s, it was thought that they subsisted on leaves and fruits, much like modern chimps. But recent findings are rewriting the anthropology texts. A careful examination of molecular traces (isotopes) left in fossilized teeth and bones suggests that the earliest humans got from 25 to 50 percent of their total calories from meat, much like

38

their caveman descendants. This suggests that our species has been omnivorous for several million years.[61] And throughout all of this time, the meat in our diet would have been low in saturated fat and calories but relatively rich in omega-3s and CLA.

This finding has important implications for the choices we make at the supermarket. According to Boyd Eaton, M.D., a leader in the field of evolutionary nutrition from Emory University, "The principles of evolutionary adaptation suggest that if a dietary pattern is maintained within a lineage for nearly two million years, it must be optimal."[62] In other words, if our species has relied on lean, omega-3 rich game for 2-3 million years, then every cell and system in our bodies will function best when we eat food with a similar nutritional profile. As you have seen, the meat from grassfed animals is very similar to wild game. Our bodies do indeed "expect" to be fed this type of food.

The Seeds of Change

The animal products in the human diet remained virtually unchanged until about four to 10,000 years ago, which is when our clever ancestors first began to cultivate cereal crops and domesticate animals. Just how recently we made the switch from wild to domesticated animals is illustrated by the following timeline. On this greatly compressed scale, one inch equals about 50,000 years. Clearly, domesticated animal products appeared on our plates very recently.

Earliest humans

▼ 3.5 MILLION YEARS AGO

PALEOLITHIC ERA

█ PRESENT TIME

↑ Domestication of Animals

Even when our ancestors began domesticating animals, however, the meat in the human diet remained virtually unchanged for several thousand additional years because the diet of the animals did not change. The farmers simply herded their animals from pasture to pasture to allow them to graze on the best grass—much as grassfarmers do today. Because the animals were still eating grass, their meat retained the nutritional profile of wild game.

But as time passed, people became more efficient at growing grain, and they began to have the luxury of feeding their surplus crops to their livestock. Grain feeding offered a number of advantages. Grainfed animals grew fatter and faster than grassfed animals, and they could be confined to a smaller space. What's more, when native grasses were stunted by heat, drought, or cold, the animals could be fed stored grain and

40

would continue to put on weight or produce milk. All seemed well in the barnyard.

Although the agricultural revolution was a time of great cultural advancement, we now know that it was a step backward in terms of nutrition. Virtually all of our so-called "diseases of civilization" including cancer, diabetes, obesity, and cardiovascular disease can be traced back to this period of history.[63] According to one source, "From studies of human skeletons from [that period] anthropologists have found clear evidence for a marked deterioration in health and mortality."[64]

The agricultural revolution succeeded in making our food supply more abundant and reliable, but the abrupt switch to a diet based on grain and grainfed animals wreaked havoc with our genes.

Technofood

Our animal products changed for the worse once again in the second half of the 20th century when fattening cattle in feedlots became commonplace. In 1947, only about 35 percent of our cattle were finished in feedlots.[65] By the 1980s, virtually all of our livestock were relegated to a "scientifically formulated diet" with its assortment of grain, chemicals, medications, and by-product feedstuff.

Given enough time, we should be able to adapt to this fat-laden, nutrient-deficient, medicated meat. But judging by the past, it may take us several million years to retool. Like most organisms, we've evolved very slowly. We last shared a common ancestor with chimps more than 5 million years ago, but we still have 98.5 percent of the same genes. We are so close in time to our Paleolithic ancestors that our genes are virtually identical.

In truth, we inhabit Stone Age bodies. When we drive to a fast-food restaurant and order a hamburger, our bodies are "expecting" the meat to have the same nutrients as wild bison, caribou, or mammoth. Although the feedlot beef may appeal to our taste buds, our bodies register a silent stream of protest: "Why so much fat? Why so many calories? Where's the CLA? I can't detect any omega-3s!!

Over time, this fat-laden, high-calorie diet takes its toll on our bodies, and we pack on the pounds, our blood pressure rises, our glucose levels soar, and we begin to fall prey to a host of degenerative diseases. To restore our health, we are advised to cut back on saturated fat and calories. This is sound advice, but it's often narrowly interpreted to mean "eat less red meat and dairy products." Thanks to the grassfarming movement, we now have a delicious alternative, one that requires little sacrifice or change in our eating habits—switch from grainfed to grassfed animal products!

﹌Chapter 5
Earth-Friendly Ranching

A growing number of people worldwide want more than a supply of wholesome food for their own consumption. They also want the assurance that the farms that created that food are not harming the environment. But one has to wonder, is there even such a thing as "earth-friendly *ranching?*"

It's a well-known fact that conventional ranching wreaks havoc with the ecosystem. What many people do not realize, however, is that much of the damage is the direct result of sending animals to feedlots and finishing them on grain. When animals spend their entire lives grazing on pasture, they leave a much smaller ecological footprint.

Consider all the problems that would be minimized if we stopped graining our cattle. Cattle are very inefficient at converting grain into meat. It takes about 8 pounds of grain to yield one pound of beef. By the time a typical feedlot steer is ready for market, it has consumed 2,700 pounds of grain—food that could have gone to feed the world's hungry.[66]

To grow all that grain conventionally requires boxcar loads of chemicals. Eighty percent of all the herbicides used in this country is applied to feedcrops such as soybeans and corn.[67] Vast amounts of chemical fertilizers are required as well. When these highly soluble chemicals are applied to row crops with their large strips of bare soil, they are vulnerable to water erosion. As much as 50 percent of the chemicals leach into our streams and groundwater.

To further increase grain production, farmers have begun to rely on genetically modified or G.M. seeds. Between 20 and 45 percent of our corn and soybeans now come from genetically altered seeds.[68] G.M. crops pose a novel threat to the environment because, for the very first time, plants themselves—not the chemicals used to treat them—may be hazardous to the biosphere. Already, there is evidence that pollen from G.M. corn is harmful to Monarch butterflies,[67] and that G.M. potatoes cause unhealthy changes in the intestines of lab animals.[70] Some fear that these new "Frankenstein" crops could lead to the evolution of pesticide-resistant insects, herbicide-resistant weeds, and virulent new plant diseases. Whether these fears are justified or not won't be known for decades.

Feeding grain to ruminants creates a gigantic logistical problem as well because the grain fields are located hundreds or even thousands of miles from the feedlots. The grain has to be shipped to the animals or the animals to the grain, using up valuable petrochemical products and further polluting the planet. It has been estimated that it takes a gallon of gas to produce one pound of grainfed meat.[71]

In the feedlots, meanwhile, the manure begins to pile up in enormous mounds because there is nothing to fertilize. One million, six hundred thousand tons of livestock wastes are produced in the United States each year.[72] Unless carefully managed, the manure leaches nitrogen into our soil, streams, and groundwater. This excess nitrogen can cause a bloom of algae and other plants that threatens marine life. Agricultural runoff is responsible for the "dead zone" in the Gulf of Mexico, an area too polluted to support marine life. In 1999, this sterile stretch of sea reached record size of 7,728 square miles.[73]

Grassfarmers are Good Stewards of the Land

Raising animals on pasture alone has a much lighter impact on the environment than conventional ranching. First of all, because grass is the primary or sole source of nourishment for ruminant animals, grassfarmers use little or no grain. When you take grain out of the equation, you also eliminate the need for genetically modified seeds and all the pesticides and chemical fertilizers used to grow the grain.

Although grassfarmers need fertile soil to grow high quality pasture, the animals fertilize the soil naturally as they graze; many farmers have been able to abandon chemical fertilizers altogether. Most farmers have stopped using herbicides as well because native weeds and plants are a welcome part of the animals' diets. Joel Salatin, a pioneering grassfarmer, refers to this nutritious mix of grasses, legumes, and wild plants as a "salad bar," and he calls his meat "salad bar beef."[74]

Another benefit of grassfarming is that it protects our streams and groundwater from agricultural run-off. Unlike row crops such as corn and soybeans, grazing land consists of a continuous carpet of plants with roots that are active nearly year round. This dense mat of vegetation absorbs soluble nutrients and protects the soil from water and wind erosion. In fact, a University of Wisconsin study found that pastures are better than any other land use for reducing runoff, erosion, and phosphorus pollution. A similar study done by the USDA-Agricultural Research Service of the North Appalachian Experimental Watershed determined that both surface and ground water in the pastured areas was just as pristine as water leaving the adjacent wooded areas.

Well-managed grazing land can benefit the environment in other ways as well. A long-term experiment on native prairie land in Kansas found that land that was grazed by bison had a richer variety of native plants than similar land that was fertilized, burned, mowed, or even left untouched.[75] Increasing plant biodiversity is a goal of environmentalists the world over.

Finally, pasture-intensive farming greatly reduces the consumption of fossil fuel. Most pastureland is planted in perennial grasses, so the John Deere tractors stay parked in the barn. And since the animals harvest their own food, the mowers and combines sit idle as well. Pasture-intensive farming is an excellent example of "low-input" sustainable agriculture.

A Revolution in Ranching

Most of the people in the grassfarming movement are dedicated environmentalists who look for additional ways to steward their land. For example, many have adopted "predatory friendly" policies that allow wild animals to co-exist with farm animals. Others have taken steps to bring back native prairie grasses or found effective fencing techniques to protect fragile streambeds from the impact of grazing animals. Additional experiments are underway to see if grazing a variety of animals on the same land can lower the population of flies and parasites and reduce the need for insecticides. For example, when pastured poultry follow after cattle in a grazing rotation, the birds devour the fly larvae deposited in the cow manure, helping to keep down the fly population and reduce the need for insecticides.

As a result of all of these efforts, grassfarmers, their families, and their neighbors get to enjoy a safe, natural environment. Farmers are not exposed to toxic chemicals. Children do not have to be kept indoors to be protected from "pesticide drift." And neighbors are treated to pastoral scenes of grazing animals—not the fetid aroma of a commercial feedlot operation. Pasture-intensive farming is a healthy way to raise a family and a healthy addition to the ecosystem.

When viewed as a whole, raising livestock on pasture is a radical departure from agribusiness as usual. As is true for any emerging industry that threatens the status quo, grassfarming has grown with little outside support. According to Allan Nation, national spokesperson for the grassfarming movement and the editor of a leading periodical, *The Stockman GrassFarmer*, "The idea of substituting pasture for grain and direct grazing for machine harvest threatens much of the current structure of North American agribusiness. Despite the opportunities it offers for tremendously increased farmer income and environmental quality, this is an industry that has had to grow in an extremely hostile and derogatory climate. That it has been able to grow, and grow rapidly indicates the underlying strength of its premise."[76]

Grassfed animal products . . . Why would you buy anything else ???

✒Chapter 6
Making the Transition to Grassfed Products

At the present time, there are about 500 farms in the United States and Canada that are marketing grassfed products to the public. This number is growing every year, but you're still not likely to find grassfed meat, eggs, or dairy products at your corner grocery store. In all likelihood, you will have to buy directly from a farm. In the resource section, we've listed detailed information on over 75 pasture-intensive farms. (Check our website— www.eatwild.com—for late additions.) Hopefully, you'll find one close to you.

If not, you'll have to do some hunting and gathering. At the present time, unfortunately, there is no universal name for grassfed animal products. They are variously described as "salad bar beef," "free-range beef," "grassfed beef," "pasture-finished beef," "pasture-ized beef," "natural beef," "Argentine-style beef," "range-fed lamb" and "New Zealand style lamb." You may have to search for all of the above.

A good place to begin is at a nearby farmers' market, especially one that features natural or organic food. Another option is to scan the classified ads in your local newspaper. The Internet can be an excellent resource because many pasture-intensive farmers market directly to the public and therefore have their own websites.

Remember, for the healthiest animals, the healthiest food, and the least impact on the environment, you're looking for farmers that raise their ruminants on fresh pasture with minimal amounts of hay or other stored forage. (Grass becomes dormant for some part of the year in most areas of the country, requiring the use of some stored hay.) Because even feedlot animals spend a significant amount of time on pasture, you need to be looking for "grass-finished," not just "grass-raised "animals. Poultry need to have constant access to fresh pasture, either by ranging freely in open fields or by being housed in moveable pens on high-quality grassland.

Keep in mind that terms such as "all-natural," "organic," "wholesome" and "like the food from Grandma's farm," do not tell you whether the ruminants have been finished on pasture or grain. You will have to ask that question directly. One way to get an honest response is to ask, "Are your animals grainfed?" Most people will assume you consider grain feeding a positive virtue. If they do feed grain, they will cheerfully tell you the amount.

A few farms listed in the resource section are midway between grassfarms and conventional farms: they finish their animals on grain, but for a shorter period of time than usual—for example, 45 or 60 days instead of the more typical 100 days. Although grain feeding an animal to any degree makes the meat higher in saturated fat and lower in CLA and omega-3s, it also makes the meat more marbled, which may appeal to customers who want a fatter, more familiar product. The choice is up to you.

Local or Mail Order?

Ideally, you will find a supplier of grassfed products in your local area. When you buy food locally, you eliminate the environmental toll caused by shipping. (The average item on your grocer's shelf traveled 1,500 miles to get there.) Buying locally also gives you a chance to see for yourself how the animals are raised.

   If you are unable to find a local supplier, you can have products shipped to you. As a general rule, only the larger farms take mail orders. Ordering through the mail will increase your overall cost, but the quality of the meat shouldn't suffer. Frozen meat that is packaged in dry ice or packed with lots of ice and shipped overnight should arrive at your door frozen solid. If not, most grassfarmers will refund your money. (Note: Some farmers won't ship their products in the hot summer months because they can't guarantee their meat will arrive still frozen.)

Organic Certification

Many pasture-intensive farms qualify for organic certification, which means that they raise their ruminants on organically certified pasture or raise their non-ruminants on a combination of organic pasture and organic grains. In addition, the animals are not treated with feed antibiotics, synthetic hormones, or other medications.

   But many grassfarms have yet to qualify for this designation. Some apply nitrogen fertilizers to their pasture or treat their animals with medications, typically to eliminate worms or other parasites. A few have been frustrated in their efforts to obtain certification for bureaucratic or logistic reasons, such as being unable to locate an organi-

51

cally certified butcher or a sufficient supply of organic grain. The realities of the marketplace have held back others. For example, a significant number of producers of pastured poultry or pigs have found that organic grain is too expensive to allow them to make a reasonable profit.

Nonetheless, most grassfarmers follow the organic model as closely as possible. Very few use insecticides, herbicides, genetically-modified grain, metabolic modifiers, by-product feedstuff, or feed antibiotics. Just because a farm lacks full organic certification, don't assume they practice agribusiness as usual. Ask.

Product Availability

Once you've located a good supplier with the products you want, your problems may not be over. Just because they have what you want, they may not have it when you want it. As you will discover, few grassfarmers manipulate their animals to force their growth or to get them to produce out-of-season. For example, most grassfed cattle, bison, and lamb are butchered at only one time of the year, typically in the fall after a summer of grazing. You may find this inconvenient if you are shopping for a fresh leg of lamb the day before Easter or T-bone steaks for the 4th of July picnic. You may have to buy a year's worth of meat in October and store it in your own freezer.

If you are buying from a small local farm, you may be further inconvenienced by having to pick up your order on a pre-arranged date. Few grassfarmers have the facilities to keep large quantities of meat chilled or frozen. If the broilers are butchered on Tuesday morning, you may have to retrieve your order by 6:00 that evening.

Finally, if you are buying from an established farm, the farm may have so many satisfied customers that you will be put on a waiting list. It's not unheard of to have to sign up for your free-range Thanksgiving turkey a year in advance!

Some of these inconveniences reflect the nascent state of the grassfarming movement. In a few years, more farms will be coming on line, and more farmers will be able to offer the amenities we've come to expect in our coddled suburban lifestyles. But some "inconveniences" are due to the dictates of nature. Our desire to have fresh meat every day of the year does not mesh with the seasonal nature of grass nor the natural breeding cycle of animals-which is one reason that most of our animals are fed artificial diets and housed under artificial conditions. If we want to have the most nutritious, environmentally friendly food, we need to learn a new way to shop.

Buying Meat for Your Freezer

When you make the transition to grassfed meat and poultry, you'll probably be buying larger quantities of meat than you have in the past and storing it in your home freezer. This brings up a lot of questions. How much meat will your household eat in a year? Should you order more hamburger or more roasts? How long will the meat keep? Butcher paper or plastic?

Some farms simplify matters by selling individual cuts of meat or moderate-sized packages of assorted cuts such as a 20-pound "grill pack" or a 15-pound "stew pack." The meat will be frozen, but the quantity is not overwhelming. But most farms sell meat only in large quantities, typically a quarter, half, or whole animal. You pay a set price per pound, usually based on the "hanging weight," which is the weight of the meat after the animal has been butchered but before it has been divided into individual cuts. The amount you take home will be 25 to 35 percent less than the hanging weight due to trimming and deboning.

The net cost of the meat will vary from farm to farm, but if you order meat in sufficient quantity, it is likely to cost about the same as ordinary meat.

The following charts show the typical yield from a hind and front quarter of beef. Many grassfarmers also offer a "split half," which is a quarter of beef that contains cuts from both the front and back quarters. (The back quarter is considered more desirable, so offering cuts from both ends is a good way to lower the cost to consumers and utilize all the meat.) Typically, halves of beef take up about 4 cubic feet of freezer space; quarters occupy half that space.

Typical Yield from a Side of Beef

Hind Quarter of Beef (144 lbs.)

Cut	Pounds
Round Steak	27.0
Rump Roast	9.9
Porterhouse, T-bone and Club Steaks	15.3
Sirloin Steak	24.9
Flank Steak	1.5
Lean Trim	21.0
Kidneys	.9
Waste (fat, bone, shrinkage)	43.5
Total Hind Quarter	**144.0**

Front Quarter of Beef (156 pounds)

Cut	Pounds
Rib Roast	18.3
Blade Chuck Roast	26.7
Arm Chuck Roast (boneless)	17.4
Brisket (boneless)	6.3
Lean Trim	49.2
Waste (fat, bone, shrinkage)	<u>38.1</u>
Total Front Quarter	**156.0**

Is Grassfed Meat Tender?

Grassfed lamb is always tender because the animals are harvested at an early age. Meat from grassfed bison and cattle can have varying degrees of tenderness, however, just like grainfed meat.

So, what makes meat tender? Most people assume that tenderness is largely due to the amount of marbling: the fatter the meat, the more tender it's likely to be. Because grassfed meat is so lean, people are worried that it's going to be tough. In reality, marbling accounts for only 10 percent of the variability in meat tenderness. Genetics accounts for another 30 percent (one of the most significant genetic factors is the diameter of individual muscle fibers.) The rest of the variability is due to a variety of other factors, including the location of the cut (loin or shoulder, for example) the age and sex of the animal, and the stress level of the animal prior to slaughter.[77] Many farmers have taken pains to maximize these "tenderness factors." Others have not. If you're not happy with the quality of your grassfed meat, shop around.

Tenderness can also be increased after the meat is harvested, most commonly by: 1) mechanical alteration, 2) marinating, and 3) dry-aging. Mechanical alteration is the pounding or grinding that produces pre-tenderized Swiss steaks, cutlets, or hamburger. Marinating, typically done at home, increases the tenderness of meat by soaking it in an acidic liquid such as wine, lemon, or vinegar. Dry aging involves holding the whole carcass at a temperature just above freezing for a week or more. This practice intensifies the flavor of the meat and also makes it more tender.

Dry aging has gone out of style because it is time consuming, and therefore not cost effective. Unless otherwise noted, all the meat you purchase at the supermarket has been "wet-aged," which means that it has been aged for a minimal amount of time in plastic. Many grassfarmers go to the extra trouble and expense to dry-age their meat so that you can have a premium product.

Cooking Grassfed Meat

Grassfed meat starts out just as tender as other meat, but it can become tough if you cook it the same way you would cook grainfed meat. The reason grassfed meat requires a special cooking technique is that it is so very lean. Fat serves as an insulator. When meat has little fat, heat is conducted more quickly and can toughen the protein. To keep grassfed meat tender, you need to cook it more slowly. If you're broiling a grassfed steak, for example, place it farther away from the heating element or coals and cook it for a longer period of time. Turn it frequently. But don't cook it too long! Even the tenderest cut of meat will become dry and tough if you overdo it.

Less tender cuts of meat such as a chuck steak or arm roast need to be cooked very slowly with moist heat. You might even want to haul your crock-pot out of the attic and try this 1970s-style cooking once again.

If you're not sure if you'll be successful at cooking grassfed meat, consider making your first order hamburger or a manually tenderized round steak. This way you can savor the rich flavor of the meat without worrying about how to cook it. (One thing you'll notice is that a pound of raw meat yields almost a pound of cooked meat; your burgers won't shrink on the grill.)

Maintaining the Quality of Frozen Meat

If you are buying a large quantity of meat for your freezer, you will want to take steps to retain its high quality. Salting meat prior to freezing shortens its storage life, but coating it with herbs and spices (without any salt) extends it. Rosemary and thyme are good herbs to use because they are potent antioxidants and help keep the meat fresh.

If you are freezing several cuts of meat in the same package, separate the meat with double sheets of wax paper to make them easier to separate while thawing.

Meat will keep indefinitely at 0° Fahrenheit or below, but the flavor and texture of the meat will suffer over time. Air is the culprit. It dries out the meat and causes freezer burn (those brownish, dry patches). Freezer burn does not make the meat unsafe to eat, but it does alter its taste and appearance.

The best way to protect the meat from air is to vacuum pack it in freezer-grade plastic bags. You can purchase a vacuum-pack food saver and package the meat yourself, or have the meat frozen and vacuum-packed by a butcher or meat locker.

If you've ordered a large amount of fresh meat, such as a quarter or side of beef, you may not be able to freeze it rapidly enough in a standard home freezer to maintain its quality. Slow freezing creates large ice crystals. During thawing, the crystals damage the cells and dissolve emulsions, causing the meat to drip and lose much of its juice. It's better to have the meat flash frozen by a butcher before you bring it home. (The rule of thumb is to freeze no more than five percent of the capacity of your freezer at any one time.)

The most common way to wrap the meat is in butcher paper, freezer foil, freezer-grade plastic bags, or plastic wrap. (When using butcher paper, the shiny side goes next to the meat.) Many butchers recommend double-wrapping. To maintain the high quality of the meat, remove as much air as possible. When using plastic bags, squeeze out the air and seal with twists or rubber bands. If you are using other types of packaging, wrap the meat tightly and tape the seams to keep out the air. Label all packages with the date, type of meat, cut, and quantity.

There are three safe ways to thaw meat: in the refrigerator; wrapped in a plastic bag and submerged in a sink or pan of cold water; or in the microwave. Thawing meat at room temperature warms the outside of the meat before the inside is completely thawed, allowing bacteria on the perimeter to multiply.

Directory of Pasture-Intensive Farms

The pasture-intensive farms listed in this section are arranged alphabetically by state. Canadian farms are listed separately at the end. Some of the farms are large enterprises that handle dozens of orders a day and ship to any state in the country. But most are small operations with limited production and facilities. Be prepared to pick up your order at the farm when prompted and bring your own plastic bags, cooler, and ice!

Note: We have not visited all the farms on this list and therefore can make no guarantee of their farming practices. Be sure to ask questions to make sure a given supplier meets all your criteria.

United States

Alabama

Goose Pond Farm specializes in pastured chickens and turkeys, eggs from free-range hens, as well as grassfed beef and lamb. The animals are free of antibiotics, growth hormones, and medications.

Goose Pond Farm, Charles and Laura Ritch, 298 Goose Pond Rd., Hartselle AL 35640. (256) 751-0987 (phone and fax). charlesritch@juno.com

Arizona

Ervin's Natural Beef is a consortium of ranchers that produces grassfed beef. Their emphasis is on humane treatment of livestock and peaceful co-existence with predators. The animals are free of pesticides, antibiotics, and synthetic hormones. The ranchers are currently applying for organic certification.

The Tucson Cooperative Warehouse distributes Ervin's Natural Beef to health food stores, co-ops and food buying groups in Arizona, New Mexico, Texas, Colorado, Utah, Nevada, and California. To locate a store or buying club in your area, see the Tucson Cooperative Warehouse website at www.tcwfoodcoop.com or call 520-884-9951. To arrange to have Ervin's beef carried by a store in your area, call the number below.   Beef jerky is available by mail.

Ervin's Natural Beef, 128 E. 19th Street, Safford AZ 85546. (520) 428-0033. http:\\www.ervins.com

Karen's Cimarron Ranch Natural Meats produces 100% grassfed beef, beef jerky (no sugar or preservatives) and pastured chicken. The animals are raised on native grass pasture. The products are available year round, subject to stock.

Karen's Cimarron Ranch Natural Meats, Karen Riggs, HCR 2 Box 7152, Willcox AZ 85643. (520) 824-3472. <u>Cimarron@vtc.net</u> <u>GREATBEEF.com</u> (GREATBEEF.com includes information about a number of producers of grass-finished beef.)

Arkansas

Blue Mountain Farm raises pastured <u>poultry</u>, <u>eggs</u> from pastured <u>chicken</u>, and <u>pork</u>. Products available include whole and half chickens and <u>turkeys</u>, boneless/skinless breast meat, legs and thighs, livers, and feet. ("About the feet-It's a long story, ask us.") The Elliots will be the first to tell you that "there are quicker, easier, and cheaper ways to raise poultry. But is it worth it? The bottom line for us is a healthy bird with plenty of down home flavor."

Blue Mountain Farm, The Elliott Family, P.O. Box 76, Fox, AK 72051. (870) 746-4704. <u>bluemtn@aristotle.net</u>

Hosanna Hills Farm has two main products at the present time: pastured <u>pork</u> and pasture-finished <u>beef</u>. The beef comes from Jersey steers ("arguably the best beef in the world") and is available by the half or quarter, but will be sold by individual cuts in the future.

Hosanna Hills Farm, Sam and Camie Ward, 406 Ward Road, Eureka Springs, AR 72631. (501) 253-5649. <u>sward@ipa.net</u>

Rivendell Gardens provides <u>pigs</u>, <u>chickens</u>, and <u>turkeys</u> raised on organically certified pasture. The chickens are available June through November; the turkeys in June, mid-October, and November. Rivendell Gardens also offers organically certified, pasture-finished <u>beef</u> each November.

Most of their products are sold by subscription to regular customers, but they have a limited amount of meat available for sale at the farm and at farmers' markets in Jasper Harrison, Arkansas. They will deliver large orders in the northwest Arkansas area.

Rivendell Gardens, Gordon and Susan Watkins, HCR 72, Box 34, Parthenon, AR 72666. (870) 446-5783. gwatkins@jasper.yournet.com

Waterfall Hollow Farm is a certified organic supplier of pasture-finished beef and lamb. The meat is free of antibiotics, synthetic hormones, feed additives, and animal by-products. The animals are never confined. The meat is USDA-inspected and vacuum packed and can be shipped anywhere in the country. VISA, MasterCard and Discover cards are "cheerfully accepted." Individual cuts are available.

The farm also offers pastured poultry and eggs. The chicken is available as whole or cut-up fryers. Most of the products are available year round. They can be found at a number of retail outlets in Arkansas. (Call for more information.)

Waterfall Hollow Farm, Dave and Lisa Reeves, 5854 Hwy 21 South, Berryville, AR 72616. (870) 423-3457. h2ofall@cswnet.com http://www.waterfallhollow.com

California

Bodega Pastures Sheep offers grassfed lamb and a wide range of organic wool products. Bodega Pastures Sheep, Hazel Flett, Box 377, Bodega CA 94922. (707) 876-3402. Internet enquiries may be directed to Joe Mortenson at jmortenson@envirolink.org www.iplex.com/cgibin/var/iplex/adler/wool/wool.html

Napa Natural Beef offers grass-finished Angus beef from Napa County, California. Produced on the Gamble Ranch, the beef is available in convenient packages for the home freezer. The beef is produced using management intensive grazing techniques to ensure healthy, biologically diverse rangeland as well as healthy cattle. Dry-aged for at least 14 days, vacuum-packed and frozen. Napa Natural Beef is available to households in San Francisco and the greater Bay Area.
Napa Natural Beef, 10 Valley West Circle, Napa CA 94558. (707) 255-4496. www.napanaturalbeef.com

Rafter "S" High Ranch Country Beef provides grassfed beef and lamb. Both types of meat are available by the whole or half carcass and also in individual cuts in clear vacuum packages.

Frozen beef is available year-round and the lamb is available in the fall while supplies last. Purchases can be made at the ranch, and mail orders are accepted "occasionally." Their products are also available at the California Certified Farmers markets in Redding, Susanville, and Montgomery Creek.

Rafter "S" High Ranch Country Beef. Mike and Linda Sawyer, P.O. Box 334, Bieber CA 96009. (530) 294-5285. rafters@hdo.net

T.O. Cattle Company sells 100% grassfed beef as split halves. (A split half will yield approximately 75 pounds of boned steaks, roasts, and ground beef.) The animals are raised on the California central coast oak savanna, and are not treated with antibiotics or synthetic hormonal implants. "Our practice is to manage ourselves, our land, and our animals wholistically."

T.O. Cattle Company, Joe and Julie Morris, 500 Mission Vineyard Rd., San Juan Bautista CA 95045. tocc@compuserve.com

Colorado

Fox Fire Farms in Ignacio, Colorado, raise free-range lambs on grass and clover pasture. The pastures are free of chemical fertilizers, pesticides, and herbicides. The lambs are not given any antibiotics, synthetic hormones, or animal by-products. They are available in whole carcasses, halves, and individual cuts and can be shipped anywhere in the United States.

Fox Fire Farms, Richard and Linda Parry, 5733 County Road 321, Ignacio CO 81137. (970) 563-4675 Fax: (970) 563-9425. foxfirefarms@frontier.net http://www.foxfirefarms.com

Hines Ranch Beef comes from animals raised exclusively on grass and forages such as alfalfa, sorghum, cornstalks, and wheat pasture. The animals are not treated with synthetic hormones, chemical fly spray, or feed antibiotics.

The grassfarmers use a controlled grazing system designed to mimic the movements of buffalo and antelope before the range was fenced. This stocking technique allows the grass to have a rest period during the growing season, helping it to reach full production. The beef is dry-aged for 12-14 days to improve tenderness and flavor. Quarters, halves, and whole carcasses are available.

Hines Ranch Beef, Chip and Judy Hines, P.O. Box 106, Kit Carson CO, 80825. (719) 962-3427.

The James Ranches faced a fork in the road in 1992. Should the three families living on the ranch turn the land into a golf course and housing development or should they devote themselves to grassfarming instead? After spending two years "discussing the future and quality of life we wanted our children and grandchildren to enjoy," they chose grassfarming.

Today, their many grateful customers rely on their grassfed <u>beef</u>, pastured <u>poultry</u>, and free-range <u>eggs</u>. The beef is available in halves, split halves, grill packages, savory packages, roasts, and ground beef packs. The Savory packages and ground beef are available year round. Splits, halves, and grill packs are available September through November. Shipping via 2-day Express Mail is "available but expensive."

James Ranches, David and Kay James, 33800 Hwy 550, Durango CO 81301. (970) 247-8836; Fax: (970) 259-0301. <u>james ranch@frontier.net</u>

Johnson Ranch has a predator-friendly policy on their grassfed <u>beef</u> ranch. They do not use antibiotics, hormones or vaccinations. Whole, halves, and split halves of beef are available, as well as lean ground beef. Their prices tend to be about 10-15 percent below grocery store retail prices.

The Johnson Ranch, Clyde, Janice, and Joel Johnson, 2823 Junction St., Durango CO 81301. (970) 247-0225.

Lasater Grasslands Beef is one of the largest pasture-intensive farms in the United States. The <u>beef</u> cattle are raised and finished on fresh pasture without artificial hormones, antibiotics, or animal by-products. The ranch is family owned and committed to sustainable agriculture and the humane treatment of animals.

A wide assortment of mail-order beef is available, including a 35# box of assorted cuts, a 15# Grill Pack Box, and various boxes of steaks, short ribs, hamburger, roasts, brisket, or tongue. Halves of beef are available as well.

Lasater Grasslands Beef ships anywhere in the United States. Orders can be placed by phone, fax, or e-mail.

LASATER GRASSLANDS BEEF, LLC, MATHESON CO 80830. (719) 541-2855; fax: (719) 541-2888. lasater@rmi.net Or visit their website and send your order electronically, http://www.lasatergrasslandsbeef.com/

Stillroven Farm raises grassfed beef in the cool, high altitude region of Colorado. The pasture, a mixture of native grasses and alfalfa, has been free of chemicals for at least three years. Pastured chicken, pheasants, and local honey are available as well. Products are available at the farm on Wednesdays and Fridays during the spring and summer, and on weekends during the winter. Call for times.

Stillroven Farm, The Gurtlers, 17629 Weld County Road 5, Berthoud CO 80513. (970) 535-4527; fax: (970) 535-0253.

Florida

Lake Oriole Ranch produces grassfed beef and eggs from pastured hens. Owner Dennis Stoltzfoos was raised on a dairy farm operated by his Amish-Mennonite family in Pennsylvania. In later years, he spent six years as an emergency medical technician, which "spawned in me an interest in health and nutrition." His early farming experiences plus his interest in nutrition have merged into the creation of his own holistic farm.

Lake Oriole Ranch, Dennis Stoltzfoos, 8483 Croom Rital Rd., Brooksville FL 34602. (352) 799-1264.

Illinois

Joy-of-Illinois is a small family farm that offers limited quantities of a wide variety of products including broiler <u>chickens</u>, <u>eggs</u>, <u>rabbits</u>, <u>lambs</u>, <u>ducks</u>, and <u>goat</u> kids. Their animals are humanely raised on pasture and are free of synthetic hormones and antibiotics.
Joy-of-Illinois, 1689 CR 400E, RR3, Champaign IL 61821. (217) 863-2758.

Indiana

The Gunthorp's Farm has pastured <u>pigs</u> and <u>chickens</u>. The animals receive no antibiotics, growth stimulants, waste fat, etc. Chickens are available from June until December. Whole, halves and split halves of pork are available for pick-up or delivery. Small quantities of pork chops, pork shoulder roasts, ground pork, bacon, and hams are also available.
The Gunthorp's Farm, Greg Gunthorp, LaGrange, IN 46761. (219) 367-2708. <u>hey4hogs@kuntrynet.com</u>

J. L. Hawkins Family Farm raises pastured <u>chickens</u> and grassfed <u>beef</u> seasonally and direct markets to customers in northeast Indiana. The beef is sold by the whole carcass, halves, or split halves. Beef quarters can also be ground into hamburger. Beef is generally ordered in March and is available for pick-up at the farm in late October or early November. Chicken is available in July and August.

J.L. Hawkins Family Farm, 10373 N 300 EN., Manchester IN 46962. (219) 982-4961 jlkawkins@kconline.com

Organic Grass Farm is a transitional farm soon to qualify for full organic certification. The farm provides grassfed chickens, turkeys, and veal, as well as eggs from pastured poultry. The cattle are moved every day to fresh grass with the use of portable electric fencing. The farm's goal is to follow a "wholistic" production model. As just one example, chickens are brought into a pasture two or three days after it has been grazed by cows so they can scratch through the cow manure and eliminate insect larvae.

The Organic Grass Farm, Melvin and Suvilla Fisher, R.R. 2, Box 244-A., Rockville IN 47872. (765) 569-5107.

Iowa

Canaan Sheep & Timber raises grassfed lamb. The meat is available as whole animals, which is approximately 50 to 60 pounds of packaged meat. The lambs are raised exclusively on pasture and hay and are available in November/ December, and March/April.

Canaan Sheep & Timber, Randall Ney, 1006 Dogwood, Wellman IA 52356 (319) 646-6696. randall-ney@uiowa.edu

Tall Grass Bison,the largest bison producer in Iowa, maintains their herd of 225 grassfed bison "as close to natural conditions as possible." The animals graze on native prairie grasses and are managed to minimize stress whenever possible. A natural family order prevails among the animals.

Humane slaughter in the field eliminates the unnecessary stress of being transported to a slaughterhouse.

Bison meat is available in halves, front quarter, hind quarter, or the 30# "Taster's Package," which is $5.00 /lb.

Bob Jackson, Bill Jackson, and Sharon Magee, P.O. Box 56, Promise City, IA 52583. (515) 874-5794.

Kansas

Jako, Inc. is one of the few grass-only dairies in the United States, which means that the milk has the maximum amount of CLA and omega-3s. The cows produce seasonally and dry up in the winter months. They are not treated with synthetic hormones, feed antibiotics, grain, or feed additives. Whole milk is available from April to mid-November at the farm. Pastured chickens and beef from the dairy cattle are also sold at the farm.

Jako, Inc., Kenneth King, 6003 E. Eales Rd., Hutchinson KS 67501. (316) 663-1470 (phone and fax) kjdking@mindspring.com   http:// www.jakoinc.com

Morrisons Grassroots Beef includes two types of meat: 1) purely grassfed beef, and 2) beef finished with a moderate amount of grain for a more traditional product. The cattle are not treated with synthetic hormones or antibiotics. Halves and split halves are available.

Morrisons Grassroots Beef, David and Beth Morrison, Morrisons Grassroots Beef, 1717 E. Stimmel Road, Salina KS 67401. (785) 823-8454. morrisonbd@informatics.net

Renaissance Farms, Ltd. has pastured Gallo-way beef (an old Scottish breed), pastured chickens, and free-range eggs. The beef and eggs are available year round. Poultry is in season from May through September, with ordering beginning in March. The products are sold at the farm. Eggs are also available at the Emporia Farmer's Market during market season.

Renasissance Farms, Judy and Bill Decker, 1800 E. 18th, Emporia, KS 66801. (316) 343-6757. anagenao@valu-line.net

Tallgrass Beef comes from the family ranches of Tallgrass Prairie Producers Co-op, a producer-owned cooperative. Their cattle are raised and finished on native grasses and other forages. The beef comes vacuum packed and pre-frozen. Write or call for more information. (Note: Sales were temporarily suspended on October, 1999 to allow time for reorganization. Call to see if sales have resumed. Mail orders may be accepted in the future.)

Tallgrass Beef, R.R. 1 Box 53, Elmdale, KS 66850. 1-800-992-5967. tallgrss@valu-line.net http://www.sunflower.com/~tallgrss

Kentucky

Au Naturel Farm is an 85-acre, certified organic grassfarm that provides grass-finished beef, available as halves or split halves. The cattle are Murray Greys, an Australian breed that "excels on grass." Pastured poultry are available by pre-order only from June to September. Free-range eggs are available from mid-February through October.

Products are sold at the farm and at the Bowling Green Farmer's Market from May through October.

Au Naturel Farm, Paul and Alison Wiediger, 3298 Fairview Church Rd., Smiths Grove KY 42171. (270) 749-4600. awiediger@Hart.k12.ky.us

Maryland

Harding Farms offers pastured eggs, chicken, beef, pork, and turkey. The beef cattle are raised on pasture alone. The poultry is raised on pasture plus a natural grain mix. The pork is raised on pasture plus out-of-date milk. Eggs are available year round. Chickens and pork are available May through October. Beef is offered in October and November. Turkey is available for Thanksgiving and Christmas. Limited quantities of all products are also available frozen at the farm. The beef and pork are sold as whole carcasses, halves, or split halves and limited individual cuts.

Harding Farms, Kelly & Anita Harding, 12329 Woodsboro Rd., Thurmont MD 21788. (301) 845-7916. hrdingfrms@aol.com http://members/ aol.com/hrdingfrms

Holterholm Farms produces pasture-finished beef from Jersey and Jersey/Angus crosses. They also offer milk from their seasonal, pasture-based dairy.

The cattle are fed some grain until they reach 300 pounds, then they receive no more grain until slaughter. Kelp is given as a natural mineral source. No antibiotics or hormones are used. The beef is available in November and December in whole carcasses, halves, split halves, and quarters.

Holterholm Farms, Ron and Kathy Holter, 5619A Holter Rd., Jefferson MD 21755-8508. (301) 371-4255. rwholter@aol.com

71

Ruth Ann's Garden Style Beef is available in whole, halves, or split halves in the spring, with the possibility of some beef being available in the fall in the future. The beef is dry-aged a minimum of two weeks, then vacuum-packed in clear plastic and quickly frozen. This 130-acre "all grass" farm is an hour from Washington D.C. or Baltimore and 20 minutes from Frederick.

Ruth Ann's Garden Style Beef, Ruth Ann and Steve Derrenbacher, 11051 Renner Rd., Woodsboro MD. 21798. (301) 898-7006. derren@cleanweb.net

Michigan

Earth Shine Farm "cuts no corners" in their efforts to produce wholesome, pastured poultry products. They offer pastured chickens fresh or frozen in season (June through October). Frozen birds are available in the winter. Their 11-year-old daughter operates a "thriving egg business." The birds are housed in moveable pens on fresh pasture and fed a special feed formula developed by Joel Salatin.

Earth Shine Farm, Laura Kay Jones, 9580 New Lothrop Rd., Durand MI 48429. (517) 288-2421.

Oak Moon Farm produces pastured chicken, turkey, and eggs plus grassfed lamb, beef and pork. Eggs, lamb, and beef are available year round. Pork is available in the fall. Lamb, beef, and pork are sold by the whole or half carcass or by individual cuts. Mail orders are accepted.

Lambs, steers, and heifers receive no grain at any point in their development. Pregnant ewes and cows may be given some grain during extreme weather conditions.

Oak Moon Farm, Jack Knorek, 22544 20 Mile Rd., Olivet MI 49076. (616) 781-3415. knorek@internet1.net

Minnesota

Cedar Summit Farm offers pastured <u>poultry</u> and <u>beef</u> raised on pasture but finished on some amount of corn, and <u>pork</u> from pigs raised in small groups. Call for more information.

Cedar Summit Farm, Dave and Florence Minor, 25816 Drexel Avenue, New Prague MN 56071. (612) 758-6886.
<u>cedarsummit@earthlink.net</u>

Dutch Mill Farm has been a certified organic farm for ten years. Grass-finished <u>lamb</u> and <u>beef</u> are available from October through December. Lambs are sold whole or by halves. Beef is available in whole carcasses, halves, and 25# family packs. Douglas Gunnink is a consultant in grassfed and organic production and can advise on fertilizers, soil amendments, seed, equipment, forage/soil testing and livestock supplies.

Dutch Mill Farm, Douglas and Janet Gunnink, 25303 461 Ave., Gaylord MN 55334. (507) 237-5162.
Fax: (507) 237-2343. <u>dgunnink@prairie.lakes.com</u>

Earth-Be-Glad-Farm offers pasture-finished <u>beef</u>, free-range <u>chickens</u>, and <u>eggs</u>. Beef is available in any quantity year round (although pasture-finished beef may be available only from September through December-be sure to ask. The meat can be sold as individually frozen cuts, beef packs (from 10-25 pounds of assorted cuts), quarter, half or whole beef. Free-range chickens are available June through November and are available whole, quartered, or cut into pieces. Processing is done at a USDA certified facility.

There are no synthetic hormones, antibiotics, or growth-promoters in any of their products. This family-run business strives to "provide the best food possible using humane and earth-friendly methods."

Earth-Be-Glad Farm, Mike, Jennifer, and Johanna Rupprecht, R.R. 2 Box 81, Lewiston MN 55952. (507) 523-2564.

Liberty Land & Livestock. This recently expanded enterprise was formerly called The Lamb Shoppe. Now it offers grassfed <u>lamb</u>, pastured <u>chicken</u> and <u>turkeys</u>, and <u>eggs</u> from free-range hens. "All of our products are raised on fresh green grass, the way nature intended."

Liberty Land & Livestock, Connie Karstens & Doug Rathke, 61231 MN Hwy 7, Hutchinson MN 55350. Phone and fax: (320) 587-6094. <u>Lambshop@hutchtel.net</u>

Mississippi

Shareef Family Pastured Poultry is a small, diversified family farm dedicated to raising pastured <u>poultry</u>, <u>sheep</u>, and <u>eggs</u>. Future products will include ground chicken sausage, <u>lamb</u>, <u>goat</u>, <u>goat's milk</u>, and <u>goat's cheese</u>. Their feed contains no antibiotics, hormones, or drugs. Organically grown fruits and vegetables may also be available.

Shareef Family Pastured Poultry, Alvin, Abdul-Hakim, and Rosa Shareef, 15 Al-Quddus Road, Sumrall MS 39482. (601) 736-0136.

Missouri

Crocket Beefmasters has not used pesticides or herbicides on their farm for over 20 years. Nor do they use antibiotics, hormones, growth stimulants, or grain of any kind. Their animals are raised exclusively on a pasture that is rich in legumes. Whole and halves of beef are available, with smaller amounts by request.

Crocket Beefmasters, 23803 Lawrence 2140, Marionville MO 65705. (417) 258-7251.

Green Hills Harvest produces <u>organic milk</u> from Jersey-cross cows. Owners Kerry and Barb Buchmayer say that a few customers have wondered if their skim and 2% milk is mislabeled because it tastes so creamy.

The Buchmayers feed their cows a limited amount of organic grain to supplement the fresh pasture. Although the cows are technically "grain-fed," they get about 1/3 to 1/2 as much grain as is typically fed in a standard dairy. The milk is hormone and pesticide free. Green Hills Harvest milk products will soon be available in select stores in the Kansas City area.

Green Hills Harvest, Kerry and Barb Buchmayer, 14649 Hwy M., Purdin MO 64674. (660) 244-5858.

Pasture-Raised Poultry offers broiler <u>chickens</u> raised in portable cages on pasture. The birds are fed organic grain when available. The Ramers also have a limited supply of pasture-raised <u>beef</u> and will raise other animals (such as <u>pigs</u>, <u>turkeys</u>, and <u>rabbits</u>) on request.

Pasture Raised Poultry, Lloyd Ramer, Rt. 1, Box 159, Rutledge MO 63563. (660) 883-5795.

Schafer Farms Natural Meats. David and Alice Schafer became involved in pasture-intensive farming in 1985 after a trip to the grassland farms of New Zealand "whacked us on the side of the head." Seeing the wisdom of the New Zealand ranching system, they came home with a keen desire to recreate grassfarming in Missouri. Now, fifteen

75

years later, their family farm offers pasture-finished <u>beef</u> and <u>lamb</u> plus pastured <u>pork</u> and chicken to mail order customers from as far away as the Middle East. "We ship as little as one lamb chop and as much as a whole steer."

Local customers can buy their products at their farm and at Wild Oats stores and select restaurants in Kansas City. You will also find limited quantities at the SunSplash Market in Naples, Florida, and Fresh Air Fare in St. Joseph, Missouri. The meat from their dairy/British cross herd is "consistently tender."

Schafer Farms Natural Meats, David and Alice Schafer, 56 S.W. 52nd Ave., Trenton MO 64683. (800) 467-5262 or (660) 359-6545.

The Semper Fidelis Ranch, established in 1979, offers pasture-raised <u>beef</u>, <u>pork</u>, and <u>chickens</u>. The Hempels grind their own grain. They do not use antibiotics or hormones. The beef is available in quantity only.

Semper Fidelis Ranch, Matthew and Albert Hempel, Rt. 1, Box 52, Eldridge MO 65463. (573) 363-5213; fax: (573) 363-5957.

Montana

Ross Peak Ranch is nestled against a national forest, which means that the land lies "downwind and downstream from no one." The Scottish Highland <u>beef</u> that graze on the pasture are available at two stores in Bozeman (Montana Harvest and Community Food Co-op) and one in Livingston (Food Works).

Meat is also available directly from the farm in whole carcasses, halves, quarters, and eights. (Approximately 400, 200, 100, and 50 pounds of beef.) Each order contains a representative sampling of cuts from the entire animal. Fifty percent of the order is ground beef. Mail orders are accepted. However, supplies are limited.

Ross Peak Ranch, Charles M. Howe, 8360 Springhill Community Rd., Belgrade MT 59714. (406) 586-8884 (phone/fax).

Thirteen Mile Farm offers mild-flavored, meaty carcasses from their predominately Corriedale grassfed <u>lamb</u>. The lambs are fed only grass, and are not treated with antibiotics, hormones or supplements. Llamas protect the sheep from predators. The meat is available as whole or half or by selected cuts. Lambs are processed at a local, USDA-inspected plant and can be shipped next-day air. Cuts are double-wrapped in freezer paper but can be vacuum-packed at your request.

Thirteen-Mile Farm, Becky Weed and David Tyler, 13000 Springhill Road, Belgrade, MT 59714. (406) 388-4945. <u>weedlamb@imt.net</u>

Nebraska

The Grain Place,Inc. offers <u>beef</u> from animals that have been raised exclusively on pasture or have been finished on grain for 30, 60 or 90 days. You get to choose. All orders must be placed by June 15th. The meat is available in split halves, halves, or whole beef.

The Grain Place, Inc., Michael R. Herman, 1904 N. Highway, Marquette NE 68854. (402) 854-3195; fax: (402) 854-2566.

McRobert's Game Farm is one of the few grassfarms in the United States that specializes in game animals. <u>Yak</u>, <u>elk</u>, <u>bison</u>, <u>deer</u>, <u>Yak/beef crosses</u>, and <u>llamas</u> are available as breeding stock. Meat is also available for sale. Yak meat is very lean and low in saturated fat. The animals are very thrifty and put on weight more easily than many other grazing animals, making them economical to raise for market.

McRobert's Game Farm, Jerry McRoberts, 55 Yak Trak, Gurley NE 69141. (308) 884-2371; fax: (308) 884-2337. jbmcrob@daltontel.net www.mcrobertsgamefarm.com

The Perfect "10" Buffalo Ranch has 5,000 acres of certified organic prairie grasses sustaining a herd of 800 grass-finished <u>bison</u>. The ranch is large enough to allow the bison to roam at will on native prairie grasses, and the herd size is sufficient to recreate the natural social order of the animals. The end result is a low stress, healthy environment similar to the open plains of hundreds of years ago.

The Hutchinsons offer their "Tatonka Gourmet Bison" in quarters, halves, and whole animals. Individual cuts, 20# packages, and summer sausage are available as well. The meat is sold in Lincoln, Nebraska at the Ideal Grocery, Aikin's Health Food Store, and Open Harvest. (The meat is distributed to other retail stores throughout the area by Pegler-Sysco Distributors.) The meat can be shipped UPS anywhere in the United States.

Perfect "10" Buffalo Ranch, Dave Hutchinson, HC 75 Box 146, Rose NE 68772. (402) 273-4574. buffalo@bloomnet.com http:// www.thebuffalomarket.com

Tar Box Hollow Buffalo Ranch raises <u>bison</u> naturally on grass. The grass-finished bison meat is available at the ranch in quantity.

Tar Box Hollow Buffalo Ranch, Rose Mason, 57957 871St Rd., Dixon NE 68732. (402) 584-2337.

The **Tucker Hill Farm** offers grass-finished lamb from February to April and pastured chickens raised the "Joel Salatin way" from June to October. (Orders for chickens are taken in the spring.) The lambs are fed fresh grass and hay only. Pastured pork and beef may be available in the future. All of their animals are free of synthetic hormones and antibiotics.

Tucker Hill Farm, Bev and Chuck Henkel, 1614 N. 61st., Norfolk NE 68701. (402) 371-5787. bchenkel@conpoint.com

New York

Bennington Beefalo. Call or write for information.

Bennington Beefalo, 1990 Stedman Rd., Attica NY 14011. (716) 591-2685.

Egg Farm Dairy is proudly "Setting the Dairy Industry back 100 Years!" The dairy was founded in 1993 by cheesemaker Jonathan White who wanted to return butter and cheese to their "lost grandeur." Currently, their Jersey cows are fed some grain, but cheese from purely grassfed cows may be available by the spring of 2001.

Egg Farm Dairy, Jonathan and Nina White, 2 John Walsh Blvd, Peekskill NY 10566. (914) 734-7343. jonathan@creamery.com
http://www.eggfarmdairy.com

Freeman Homestead offers pastured chickens and turkeys, grassfed beef, pork, and lamb. They also sell eggs from free-ranging hens and ready-to-lay pullets (in season).

The Freemans welcome visitors interested in their alternative methods of farming.

Freeman Homestead, Keith and Rae Ellen Freeman, 1355 28th Creek Rd., Kennedy NY 14747. 287-2056.

Oswego County Beef Producers is an organization of grassfed <u>beef</u> producers in upstate New York. For information about available products and individual suppliers, call (315) 963-7286 or write to Oswego County Beef Producers, Cornell Cooperative Extension of Oswego County, 3288 Main Street, Mexico NY 13114.

Sap Bush Hollow Farm offers a wide variety of pasture-raised products, including <u>chicken</u>, <u>beef</u>, <u>lamb</u>, <u>turkeys</u>, <u>pork</u>, <u>sausage</u>, and <u>bacon</u> that are free from hormones and antibiotics. Adele and Jim Hayes have been practicing rotational grazing and sustainable agriculture since 1979. Their goal is "to produce the best animals under the most natural conditions we can achieve with our resident plant and animal life mutually benefiting from our efforts."

The meat is available in individual cuts or whole, half or split-half carcasses. Lamb, beef, pork, and veal are available frozen year round. The poultry is seasonal.

Sap Bush Hollow Farm, Adele and Jim Hayes, HCR #1 Box 152, Warnerville NY 12187. (518) 234-2105 or <u>sapbush@aol.com</u>

Seldom Seen Farm specializes in heritage breeds-Bourbon red <u>turkeys</u>, Soay <u>sheep</u>, Dexter <u>cattle</u>, Wyandotte <u>hens</u>. "These were the breeds that your grandma might have had in years gone by." These rare breeds were selected to preserve our heritage and because they are especially well adapted to grazing.

Free-range <u>eggs</u> are available year round.

Pastured broilers are sold from June through November. Lamb, pork, and beef are available by order as available. "We strive to be as organic as possible, using homeopathic remedies where possible and only resorting to conventional medications when the health of the animal is at risk."

Seldom Seen Farm, Pamela and James Marshall, P.O. Box 351, Amenia NY 12501. (914) 373-7207. caiplichhorses@hotmail.com

Sweet Grass Farm provides grassfed lamb, veal, pork, and eggs from pastured hens. The lamb and veal are available from July to November at the farm. Some of the grazing animals are fed grain and some are strictly grassfed. Please inquire.

Sweet Grass Farm, Wendy Gornick, 5537 Cooper St., Vernon NY 13476. (315) 829-5437. wgornick@borg.com

ZuZu Petal's Farm strives to eliminate the gap between producer and consumer. "We encourage our customers to visit our farm and see how our animals are raised." The farm offers pastured poultry, eggs from pastured hens, grass-finished lamb and beef. Their beef comes from Scottish Highland Cattle and their lamb from Jacobs Sheep. Both are conservancy breeds, rare breeds that are facing extinction. The products are available at the farm and at Ithaca's Farmer's Market in the summer and fall.

ZuZu's Petals Farm, Pam Millar, 439 Dawson Hill, Spencer NY 14883. (607) 589-4762. millarjs@clarityconnect.com

Ohio

Cass Stock Farm Herefords are raised on pasture but are also fed some grain that is grown on the farm. The animals are not given synthetic hormones, antibiotics, or chemical additives of any kind. Mixed packages of beef are available from 20 to 105 pounds. (Steaks and roasts comprise 2/3 of the total weigh; lean ground <u>beef</u> makes up the other 1/3.)

The Cass Stock Farm, Ron and Sharon Cass, Box 402, Caledonia OH 43314. (419) 845-3823.

McNutt Farm cattle are raised on open pasture, with grass hay fed in the winter season months. The animals are a mixture of shorthorns and Brown Swiss, and their meat is free of hormone and antibiotics. Ground <u>beef</u> and individual cuts are available.

The McNutt Farm, 6120 Cutler Lake Road, Blue Rock OH 43720. (740) 674-4555.

Oklahoma

Redbird Ranch has been chemical-free for 15 years. The farm is managed using holistic principles, and all the animals are handled using low stress methods.

Pastured broilers are available in the spring, summer, and fall. Eggs are available throughout the year, with a limited supply in the winter. Beef is harvested in the early fall and is available as whole, halves, and quarters. The meat is cut and wrapped to your specifications. The beef comes from Dexter and Dexter-cross animals, an old Irish breed that is smaller than most. (A quarter of beef weighs approximately 100 pounds.)

Redbird Ranch, Mark and Erin Parman, Rt 1, Box 443, Webbers Falls, OK 74470. (888) 608-

4720. redbird@crosstel.net

Oregon

CMS Sheep Company offers <u>lamb</u> at two times of year. The fall lambs are fed a small amount of grain in addition to grass. The spring lambs are finished on clover and grass only.

Pastured <u>pork</u> is available in the fall. A limited supply of <u>beef</u> is available from Jersey cows or dairy cross calves that are butchered in June after grazing on the spring grass. The beef is available in halves or whole.

CMS Sheep Company, Scott and Margaret Sublette, 1099 Elkhead Rd., Yoncalla OR 97499. (541) 849-2871.   sublette@wanweb.net

The Graf Century Farm has been in the family for over 100 years. Several years ago, Nita and Loren Wilton began making the transition to pasture-intensive farming. Today they raise pasture-finished beef,as well as pastured <u>chickens</u>, and <u>turkeys</u> on certified organic pasture. Soon, they will be offering eggs from pastured hens as well.

The Wiltons' goal is to practice an agriculture that "heals and regenerates, and that thrives on diversity, resource regeneration, and lower petroleum use." As an example of their holistic approach, they use "composting pigs." After the cattle have been returned to pasture in the springtime, pigs are brought into the winter shed to root around in the cattle's winter bedding. Within weeks, the rooting pigs have aerated the bedding and turned it into sweet-smelling compost. The finished compost is spread back on the pasture, returning the nutrients to the soil.

83

Pasture-finished beef is available in whole, half, or split-halves (quarter) on a seasonal basis. Turkeys are available in the fall, and batches of chickens are processed at intervals throughout the year. Order early.

The Graf Century Farm, Nita and Loren Wilton, 44222 S.E. Louden Rd., Corbett OR 97019. (503) 695-5452.

Kneedeep Grass & Cattle Company produces grass-finished <u>beef</u> and pastured <u>chicken</u> and <u>turkeys</u>. The beef is available in halves or whole, or in individual cuts with a 100-pound minimum order. Ground beef is available in orders of 25 pounds or more.

The freezer beef is available September through November. Ground beef is available July through November. Broiler chickens are sold from July through September, with turkeys available in October. Meat is also available at Naturally Yours Health Food Stores in Hermiston and John Day, Health Haven Foods in Pendleton, and Randy Smith's in Bremerton, Washington. The frozen meat can be shipped Second-Day Air anywhere in the United States.

Kneedeep Grass & Cattle Co., Ken and Connie Pond, 302 SW 23rd St., Hermiston OR 97838. (541) 567-4470. <u>pondk@oregontrail.net</u>

Mandala Farms Beef is a two-farm cooperative with a goal of delivering "a product as pristine as wild meat, but with the added flavor and texture benefits that have been bred into British cattle since the early days of the Industrial Revolution." The Red Angus and Herefords raised on the ranch have "100 percent pure British bloodlines." They are harvested at 20 months of age or less. The grassfed <u>beef</u> is dry-aged and then cut and

84

wrapped according to customer instructions.

Mandala Farms, 45404 Notch Rd., Fossil OR 97830.

River Run Farm offers organic, pasture-finished <u>beef</u> from Black Angus cattle. The meat is dry-aged for a minimum of two weeks. The meat is available at the farm in individual cuts. People who are interested in larger quantities should call and inquire. The meat is also sold at the Portland Farmer's Market and can be delivered to Portland area residences on an occasional basis. River Run beef is featured at Higgins' Restaurant, a fine restaurant in Portland.

River Run Farm, James and Ellen Girt, 19224 Swedetown Rd., Clatskanie OR 97016. (503) 728-4561. <u>egirt@aone.com</u>

Pennsylvania

Canyon Livestock Company raises <u>beef</u> cattle under two different systems. Animals that end the summer weighing 700 pounds or more are butchered early in the fall, making grass their sole source of nourishment. Those that weigh less than 700 pounds are over-wintered on a diet of hay and some grain. In early spring, they are returned to the pasture to be finished on grass. (All animals are butchered before their second spring.) The beef is available in quantity only.

Canyon Livestock Company, R.D. #6, Box 205, Wellsboro PA 16901. (570) 724-7788.

Double G Farm offers pastured <u>poultry</u> and <u>eggs</u> from pastured hens. Barb and Kevin Gorski applied for a SARE grant to determine the nutritional benefits of their poultry products and discovered that their broilers have 21 percent less total fat, 30 percent less saturated fat, and 28 percent fewer calories than ordinary chicken. Their eggs are richer in vitamin A and much lower in cholesterol than factory eggs.

Their products are available from June through October at their farm. The Gorskis ship their products within Pennsylvania.

Double G Farm, Barb and Kevin Gorski, 227 Henne Rd., Bernville PA 19506. (610) 488-6555.

Dr. Elkins' Angusburger, unique among the pasture-intensive enterprises, sells most of its meat as pure ground <u>beef</u>. All cuts except the loin and rib go into this premium product. Angusburger is made from Angus steers raised from birth until market on pasture. The animals are not treated with hormones or antibiotics. The ground beef comes frozen in one-pound packages wrapped in cryovac. When tested for its nutritional content, the meat is consistently high in omega-3 fatty acids and CLA.

Dr. Elkins' Angusburger, 3575 Doe Run Church Rd., East Fallowfield PA 19320. (610) 486-0789. Elkins32@aol.com

Forks Farm supplies pasture-finished beef, pastured pork, grass-finished lamb, and pastured chickens and turkeys for over 100 families.

Their beef is from prime, young Angus/ Hereford cattle that "are allowed to grow naturally on protein-rich forage." The beef is available in wholes, halves, and quarters. "Order enough to get you through the year." Chickens are available in the summer months. Turkeys are available in early November. Lambs are processed in September and beef are available from mid October until early November.

Forks Farm, The Hopkins Family, RR2, Box 193-B, Orangeville PA 17859. (570) 683-5820.

Marwood Farm offers eggs from free-range birds, pastured chickens and turkeys, and grassfed beef in limited quantities. Pasture-finished beef is available by the halves, split halves (quarter) or by the individual cut. Fresh bread may be available on pick-up days.

Marwood Farm, Donald and Christine Scott, 1068 Woodstock, Fayetteville PA 17222. (717) 352-7090.

Overlook Farm has grassfed beef that is free of synthetic hormones and antibiotics. The meat is sold by the half, quarter, and ground quarter. Call or write for more information.

Rob and Alanna Reed, 233 Spruce Road, Karns City PA 16041. (724) 756-0540.

Things Eternal Farm provides pastured pork and poultry. The chickens are housed in bottomless cages that are moved daily, and the pigs are kept in portable cages that are relocated "when the pigs are done tilling the soil." Chickens are available monthly from May through October, pork in April and September. Organically raised vegetables are available seasonally. The farm is within a 50-mile radius of the greater Washington/Baltimore area.

Things Eternal Farm, Randy Simpson, 3489 Bullfrog Road, Fairfield PA 17320. (717) 642-6450. bullfrog@wideopen.net

WIL-AR Farms is a small, family farm with limited amounts of a broad range of products including grassfed beef, veal, lamb, rabbits, pork, chickens, turkeys, eggs, butter, yogurt and cream. In the future, they may be adding cheese to this extensive menu.

The Newswangers strive to farm in harmony with the seasons. "Cycling our production with nature's seasons must not be compromised. As soon as we produce food against the seasons, disease, costs, and environmental degradation escalate. We calve when the deer are fawning, start chicks when the wild turkey eggs are hatching, and increase our workload when the days are longer."

WIL-AR Farms, Wilmer and Arlene Newswanger, 76 Parker Rd., Newville PA 17241. (717) 776-6552.

South Carolina

Crusader Farms offers pastured <u>chickens</u> and <u>turkeys</u>, <u>lamb</u>, <u>eggs</u> from free-range birds, and <u>beef</u> from cattle that are a Scottish Highlander/ Shorthorn cross. (The Highland/Shorthorn cross won the top prize at the Denver National Stock Show 21 out of 25 years.) The basic tenet of Crusader farms is to "have as near to perfect soil as possible... This means that our cattle, sheep, chickens and turkeys will make the best gain on fresh forage, and we will not have to feed them grains and fillers."

Crusader Farms, P.O. Box 1312, Anderson SC 29622. (864) 296-4541.

Greenbrier Farms raises <u>beef</u> cattle that are a Senepol/Angus cross, resulting in "natural tenderness and great taste." The meat is not only "free-range, it's free of animal by-products, growth hormones and antibiotics." The meat is dry-aged 14 days.

The owners, John and Joyce Palmer, have brought in llamas to guard their cattle and goats to control their weeds "so that you enjoy beef that is herbicide free."

Greenbrier Farms, John and Joyce Palmer,

772 Hester Store Rd., Easley SC 29640. (888) 859-0125/(864) 859-0125.

Tennessee

Peaceful Pastures All Natural Meats provides chickens, turkeys, pork, lambs. dairy goats, kid goats, veal, and beef. The sheep are raised exclusively on pasture. The dairy goats get some grain while they are lactating. The veal calves and late beef calves also get some grain. Adult cattle get no grain. Fleece from their Lincoln Longwool sheep are available for hand spinning and felting.

Beef, cut to customer specifications, is available in June through December. Veal is available from July to November. June is the month for lamb. "We highly recommend a deposit well in advance." Chicken is available June through November.

Peaceful Pastures All Natural Meats, Darrin and Jenny Drake, 69 Cowan Valley Lane, Hickman, TN 38567. (615) 683-5556. Peacepast@aol.com

Texas

Homestead Healthy Foods has a number of products available, including pastured beef and chicken, smoked beef, and summer sausage. Beef is available in individual cuts. The chickens are fed a supplemental feed ration that contains organic flax oil, a source of omega-3 fatty acids. They also forage on grass.

Meat is delivered to Austin, Texas, once a week, and shipping to other locations is also available. Call for details. The Sechrists have a Cooking Guide that includes some of their favorite recipes for grassfed beef.

Richard and Peggy Sechrist, Homestead Healthy Foods, Rt. 2, Box 184-A, Fredericksburg

TX 78624. (830) 997-2508 or toll free (888) 861-5670. http://www.homesteadhf.com

Slanker's Polled Herefords supplies 100% pasture-finished <u>beef</u>, as well as performance tested breeding bulls. The grassfed beef is available in late spring and fall at the ranch in Powderly, Texas. Call to inquire about shipping possibilities.

Slanker's Polled Herefords, Ted Slanker, RR 2, Box 175, Powderly TX 75473. (903) 732-4653. slanker@neto.com
www.neto.com/slanker/top.htm

The Texas Bison Company is headquartered at the Moseley Ranch in the Blackland prairie of northeast Texas. The Moseleys specialize in grass-finished <u>bison</u> raised on native prairie grasses. The animals are not treated with hormones or antibiotics and are harvested at a young age. "We pride ourselves on the quality of our bison meat while using low input sustainable farming methods and intensive grass management. No pesticides or herbicides are used! Instead, we rely on haying, grazing, and burning to maintain our plant communities."

The meat is sold by individual cut, subject to availability. It is available at the ranch, at select stores in the Dallas/Ft. Worth area, and by mail order. The meat can be shipped anywhere in the United States. Ranch tours can be arranged.

Jan and Austin Moseley, Texas Bison Company, 3582 County Road 2150, Caddo Mills TX 75135. (903) 527-2325. jmoseley@webwide.net
http://www.bisonranch.com

Utah

Ensign Ranches is a large cattle and wildlife operation that is working to preserve open spaces and to support ranchers who are devoted to improving their land.

"We are currently developing a business plan to produce grassfed beef on a large scale to meet the needs of more customers and to reward ranchers for their commitment to the environment. Please contact us if you are interested in joining this effort."

Grassfed <u>beef</u> will be available by the summer of 2000. Ensign Ranches also offers a workstudy program, ranch tours, and hunting opportunities for deer, elk, and moose.

Ensign Ranches of Utah, Gregg Simonds, 6315 No. Snowview Dr., Park City, UT 84086. (435) 647-9134; fax: (435) 647-9821. <u>jsimonds@uswest.net</u>

Vermont

The Flack Family Farm produces pasture-raised and finished <u>lamb</u> on certified organic fields. The lamb is available for sale at the farm and at the Onion River Co-op in Burlington. It is also featured at a number of local restaurants.

The meat is available as whole lamb, cut to your specifications, or in individual cuts. Sausage and salami can be ordered as well. The lamb can be shipped anywhere in the United States.

The Flack Family Farm, RD 2, Box 900, Enosburg Falls VT 05450. (802) 933-7752. Fax: (802) 933-6148. <u>Bflack@lamoille.k12.vt.us</u> <u>http://www.together.net/~bflack</u>

The Hill Farm of Vermont specializes in organically certified, pasture-raised <u>beef</u>. (To qualify for organic certification, animals must get 100% organically grown feed and cannot be treated with drugs, hormones, or wormers.)

Beef is sold by the whole, half, and quarter, based on its hanging weight. Halves range from 160 to 220 pounds and take up about 4 cubic feet of freezer space. Hamburger and stew meat from older animals is available at a lower cost.

Large quantities of beef are available in October at the farm or direct from the butcher. Their "hamburger special" is available at various times throughout the year.

Hill Farm of Vermont, Peter Young and Nancy Everhart, RD 1, Box 740, Plainfield VT 05667. (802) 426-3234.

Virginia

Big Oak Angus Beef is pasture-raised and free of chemicals. The animals are processed at a younger age than conventional <u>beef</u> to insure their tenderness. The beef comes vacuum-sealed to preserve its freshness.

Big Oak Angus Beef, the Jerry Smith Family, Riner VA (540) 382-7284.

The Bright Farm has pastured chickens and turkeys, pork, and eggs from free-range hens. The beef is available in whole, halves and split halves (quarters) and is sold by hanging weight.

The Bright Farm, Larry and Debby Bright, 794 Spangler Mill Rd. N.E., Floyd VA 24091. (540) 745-5790.

Burke's Garden Farmers' Alliance offers a range of products including grassfed <u>beef</u> and <u>lamb</u>

and pastured <u>poultry, pigs</u>, and <u>eggs</u> from free-range hens. The beef and lamb are available in halves in the fall. Whole chickens are available from May to October. Eggs are available throughout the year, with limited quantities in the winter. Pork is available in whole carcasses in the fall. Products are available at the farm and by overnight delivery.

Burke's Garden Farmers' Alliance, P.O. Box 444, Burke's Garden VA 24608. (540) 472-2535. <u>gswhitted@inetone.net</u>

Good Earth Organic Farm is the research and demonstration arm of Good Earth Publications. The farm offers pasture-raised <u>beef</u>, <u>pork</u>, <u>chickens</u>, <u>turkeys</u>, <u>eggs</u>, and <u>meat goats</u>. The meat is available by the pound, quarter, halves, or whole. The ruminants are on pasture from birth, and the poultry is on pasture as soon as it leaves the brooder.

The food is sold at the farm, via the Internet, at restaurants, stores, farmers' markets, and through Community Supported Agriculture (CSA). Farm tours, field days, workshops, and apprenticeships through the Good Earth Farm School are available.

Good Earth Publications, Andy Lee and Patricia Foreman, Good Earth Organic Farm, 1702 Mountain View Rd., Buena Vista VA 24416. (540) 261-8775. <u>goodearth@rockbridge.net</u> <u>www.goodearthpub.com</u>

Meadow Creek Dairy practices management intensive grazing with their herd of Jersey cows. They use no herbicides or pesticides on their land. "Our only crop is grass. We are therefore able to provide excellent nutrition for our herd while improving the health and fertility of our land." The cows' diet consists of perennial grasses supplemented with some grains, salt, and Norwegian kelp.

Meadow Creek Dairy is a licensed, inspected cheese plant. Their cheeses include Appalachian jack, double-aged jack, and Meadow Creek feta.

Meadow Creek Dairy, The Feete family, 6380 Meadow Creek Road, Galax VA 24333. mcd@ls.net   http://www.ls.net/~mcd

Pearce and Lori Gardner provide pastured rose veal and pork. Broilers are available from May through October, and eggs can be purchased year round.

Pearce and Lori Gardner, 558 Bowlers Road, Tappahannock VA 22560. (804) 443-1010. gpromo@access.digex.net

Polyface, Inc is grassfarming guru Joel Salatin's family farm. Nestled in Virginia's Shenandoah Valley, the farm was launched in 1961 by Joel's health-conscious parents. The family has never used chemical fertilizers, pesticides, or herbicides, making this one of the oldest environmentally friendly farms in the United States. Polyface has been the working model for many of the farms in this directory.

Four hundred families and numerous restaurants rely on Polyface for salad bar beef, eggs from free-ranging hens, ready-to-lay pullets, and pastured chickens, turkeys, rabbits and pigs. Some customers drive 300 miles round trip to pick up their products.

It may be inconvenient for customers to have to drive to the farm, but there's a hidden benefit: they get to see exactly how their food was raised. Children may benefit the most. According to Joel, "Kids enjoy seeing and petting the animals, romping in the fields, and learning firsthand who, what, where, when, why, and how their food was made."

Polyface, Inc., The Salatins, Rt. 1, Box 281, Swoope, VA 24479. (540) 885-3590.

Thorntree Farm is a small family farm located at the foot of the Clinch Mountains in Virginia. Their black Angus cattle were selected for their excellent beef qualities and their pleasant dispositions. The cattle are raised naturally on fresh grass without hormones or antibiotics to stimulate their growth. The meat is vacuum-packed and quick frozen for your convenience. "You can purchase as little as a pound of ground beef or a whole or half carcass."

Thorntree Farm Beef, Rt. 2, Box 776A, Nickelsville, VA 24271. (540) 479-3057; fax: (540) 479-3422.

Washington

Oyster Bay Farm offers lamb from animals that were fed small amounts of grain. It is available in the fall "just as the rains are making our pasture too wet for grazing."

Lamb is available as whole or half carcasses. Most lambs dress out to a hanging weight of 50 pounds. You pick up your packaged, frozen lamb at the butchers when they call and tell you it's ready. Typical cost for a lamb with a hanging weight of 50 pounds is about $140, which translates into $3.50 a pound for a take-home weight of 40 pounds.

Oyster Bay Farm, 4931 Oyster Bay Rd., N.W., Olympia WA 98502. (360) 866-9424.

Wisconsin

Cattleana Ranch offers pasture-finished Galloway beef and free-range chickens. The beef is processed through a state-certified, family-run butcher shop. "You will always know where your beef has been raised and processed."

The chickens are available on a seasonal basis. Orders of six birds and more must be placed by June 15. Pick-up is in mid-summer and early fall.

The beef is packaged in a variety of 20-pound boxes. For example, the "Executive Box" contains T-bone, Porterhouse, rib eye, sirloin, and cube stakes, plus one rolled rump roast. The "Grill Pack" has sirloin and cube steaks plus hamburger, homemade wieners, and summer sausage.

Cattleana Ranch, Thomas and Susan Wrchota, 5200 O'Reilly Rd., Omro WI 54963. (920) 685-6964.

Northstar Bison is a family owned and operated business that encompasses several hundred acres near the Blue Hills of northwestern Wisconsin. Their premium, grassfed <u>bison</u> include breeding stock from nationally recognized sources. All cuts, from burger to tenderloin, including convenience foods, are available at the store on their ranch. Shipping is available year round. Scenic tours can be arranged.

Northstar Bison, 1936 28th Ave., Rice Lake WI 54868. (715) 234-0045 or (715) 234-9085. http://www.northstarbison.com

Four Winds Farm offers pasture raised <u>beef</u>, <u>pork</u>, and <u>chicken</u>. The cattle graze on grass-legume pastures in the summer and standing corn and hay in the winter. Chickens are raised seasonally on pasture.

Pork and beef are available by the quarter or by individual cuts. Other products include all-beef hot dogs, wood-smoked summer sausage, beef jerky, ground beef patties, and other pork products. The food is available at the farm and at the food co-op in River Falls. Interstate shipping to be available soon. Farm tours available by appointment.

Four Winds Farm, Juliet Tomkins, N8806 600th St., River Falls WI 54022. (715) 425-6037. 4winds@win.bright.net

Saxon Homestead Farm has 350 pastured dairy cows producing <u>milk</u> and 70 <u>bison</u>. This fifth generation farm has transitioned in the past 20 years from a "conventional concrete dairy" to 900 acres of grassland. The owners are half way through the organic certification process. Plans for making farmstead cheese and selling their bison meat and cheese at their own farm store is in the works. Call for current product information. Saxon Homestead Farm, Gerald and Elise Heimerl, 15621 S. Union Rd., Cleveland WI 53015. (920) 693-8300.

Snowy Fields Farm is a family enterprise that offers a wide variety of products. All of their animals are raised humanely without synthetic hormones, antibiotics or "anything you can't pro-nounce."

The <u>beef</u> comes from dairy steers that are a minimum of two years of age. The <u>lambs</u> are Jacob and Jacob crosses-rare breeds that "produce excellent quality meat." The <u>veal</u> comes from calves hand-raised on milk from their cows. <u>Pork</u> comes from Tamworth pigs "when available." <u>Chevron</u> (young goat) is a new addition. Free-range <u>chickens</u> are available one to three times a year. Beef, lamb, pork, and veal are sold by the whole or halves. Beef can be sold by quarters "provided you can find someone to share the other quarter."

Snowy Fields Farm, 407 310 St., Wilson WI 54027. (715) 772-3175 ficken@win.bright.net

CANADA

Alberta

Deer Creek Ranch The Gilchrist family of Deer Creek Ranch invites you to enjoy the great taste and superior health benefits of their grass-finished beef. "Historically, our grazing lands have supported vast herds of bison, and our cattle now enjoy the benefit of the very nutritious forage at the foot of the Sweetgrass Hills of southern Alberta.

The beef is available in halves and split halves, cut to order. Sausage and jerky are sold as well. Deadline for orders is August 15, and the beef is available in October and November.

Deer Creek Ranch, Neal Gilchrist and Dr. Susan Lea, Box 86, Milk River, AB, T0K 1M0 Canada. (403) 647-2200. swtgrass@telusplanet.net

Hoven Farms provides certified organic beef, chicken, turkeys, and eggs. The cattle are raised on pasture year-round with supplementary feed in the winter. All animals have forage available year round. Beef and chicken are available throughout the year. Chickens are offered in the summer (until they sell out) and turkeys can be purchased at Thanksgiving. The animals are available in all sizes from whole carcasses to individual cuts.

Hoven Farms, Peter Hoven, RR#3, Eckville AB Canada T0M 0X0 Canada. (800) 311-2333/ (403) 746-3072. peter@hovenfarms.com www.hovenfarms.com

Sunworks Farm offers pastured poultry from chickens that forage on organically certified pasture. The birds are not given any drugs and there are no chemical additives, animal by-products or hormones in their feed.

"We at Sunworks Farm base our farming decisions on holistic principles. . . Our grazing practices promote preservation of wildlife habitat. We are predator friendly, using llamas to keep predators at bay."

Sunworks Farm, Box 55, Armena, AB T0B 0G0 Canada. To order, call toll free (877) 393-3133 or 672-9799. sunworks@telusplanet.net

British Columbia

Dave & Pat Griffith have a family-based business raising chickens, turkeys, pigs, cattle, and goats. All of the animals are raised on pasture and are not fed any hormones, pesticides, herbicides, or medicated feed.

Chickens are available from July 1st to October 5th (whole birds only). Turkeys are sold in October. Pork and beef are available year round in halves or whole carcasses. (Beef is also available as hamburger by the pound.) Goat is available in whole carcasses.

Dave and Pat Griffith, Box 1942, Vanderhoof BC V0J 3A0. Canada. (250) 567-2860 ebus292@uniserve.com

Manitoba

Mother Nature's Beef "raises the beef cattle to suit what the final customer requires." You can specify if you want antibiotics withheld, whether the animals are finished on grain or grass, and the age and breed (within limits) of the animal. Most of the cattle are sold at about 850 pounds. Shipping is available.

Mother Nature's Beef, Ml. Masserini, P.O. Box 34, Lake Francis, MB R0C 1T0 Canada. (204)

383-5828. ml.masserini@wanadoo.fr

Ontario

Webers' Pasture Farm has a goal of producing "the highest quality food for our customers without chemicals, hormones, medications, or genetic engineering." Their products include salad bar (pasture-finished) beef, grassfed lamb, pastured pork, eggs from free ranging hens, and pastured chickens. The owners strive to be "good stewards of the land and encourage biodiversity."

Webers' Pasture Farm, Marvin and Amanda Weber, R.R. #2, Dobbinton ON N0H 1L0 Canada. (519) 934-9906.

Saskatchewan

Bennett Beef markets pasture-finished beef. The Bennetts, like most grassfarmers, practice "management intensive grazing." Their farm is divided into 50 separate fields called "paddocks," which allows the animals to be rotated every day or so to clean, fresh grass. This "pulsed" grazing helps create optimum growth of the grass.

The meat is harvested in October and is available in halves or in smaller quantities by arrangement. Orders are taken throughout the year. "We encourage you to place your order early to avoid disappointment."

Bennett Beef, Box 60, Meacham, SK S0K 2V0. Canada. (306) 944-4340.

Daleview Farm is located in the middle of grain country in Saskatchewan, but the Dales valiantly produce grassfed beef, pork and poultry. "We're really bucking the tide." They first started pasturing their animals many years ago as a way to cut costs. Then they began to notice the many benefits to the animals and to their own health. Now they are committed grassfarmers with a holistic approach to ranching.

Most of the meat is available in the fall only. Beef is available in halves or whole carcasses. Daleview Farm, John and Karen Dale, Box 75, Meacham SK S0K 2V0 Canada. (306) 944-4241.

Publications Relevant to Grassfarming

ACRES U.S.A. is a monthly periodical devoted to organic farming and gardening. This "voice for eco-agriculture" is $24 a year. Call toll free in the US and Canada, 1-800-355-5313. Visit their website at http://www.acresusa.com

APPPA Grit is a quarterly newsletter published by the American Pastured Poultry Producers Association. Grit promotes the exchange of ideas and information about pastured poultry, including legal issues regarding on-farm poultry processing, information on chicken feed, rations, new/used production and processing equipment, marketing, referrals, and sources of chicks. To join, send $20 to APPPA, c/o Diane Kaufmann, 5207 70th Street; Chippewa Falls, WI 54729 (715) 723-2293

Backyard Market Gardening by Andy Lee, Most of the grassfed animal products raised in this country at this time are sold directly to the consumer. This book helps small farms develop their market. Published by Good Earth Publications. (Visit their website at goodearthpub.com) ISBN 0-9624648-0-5

The Chicken Tractor, by Andy Lee and Pat Foreman. This book provides practical information on a variety of ways to house chickens on pasture or in your suburban garden. You are even given instructions on how to build a chicken coop out of straw bales. Published by Good Earth Publications.

Grass Productivity by André Voisin revolutionized ranching in 1959 when this classic was first published. Voisin's novel idea: Don't study the grass by itself or the animals by themselves. Study the interaction between grazing animals and the grass. "Grazing," he says simply, "is the meeting of cow and grass." If you want to understand more about this symbiotic relationship, begin with *Grass Productivity*. Published by Island Press. ISBN 0-933280-64-5

Moving 'Em by Dr. Burt Smith. Burt Smith is an extension specialist in pasture and livestock management at the University of Hawaii. His 352-page book teaches low-stress techniques for handling large animals. This book introduces the basic concepts and includes practice sessions complete with diagrams. Smith says that the most satisfying aspect of low-stress handling is "working with animals, instead of on them."

Pastured Poultry Profits by Joel Salatin has been the how-to-manual for most of the farmers in the pastured poultry business. To quote Allan Nation, "All of us interested in seeing an American rural revival should thank Joel and Teresa Salatin for going to the effort and expense to share their experiences and recommendations for pastured poultry." Published by Polyface, Inc., Swope Virginia. Polyface, Inc., The Salatins, Rt. 1, Box 281, Swoope, VA 24479. (540) 885-3590.

Quality Pasture, How to create it, manage it, profit from it, by Allan Nation. There's far more to growing quality pasture than you would have ever imagined, and Nation knows all the tricks. Published by Green Park Press, a division of the Mississippi Valley Publishing, Corp., Jackson, Mississippi. 285 pages. (800) 748-9808

Salad Bar Beef is Joel Salatin's step-by-step instruction manual for raising pasture-finished cattle. In this 368-page book, he presents detailed information on grazing philosophy, breed selection, handling facilities, electric fencing, paddock layout, and a host of other practical matters. .Published by Polyface, Inc., Swope Virginia. Polyface, Inc., The Salatins, Rt. 1, Box 281, Swoope, VA 24479. (540) 885-3590.

The Stockman GrassFarmer is the leading periodical for the grassfarming movement. Farmers wait eagerly for Allan Nation's monthly publication to gain new insights and practical advice about this enlightened method of farming. The Stockman GrassFarmer is the glue that holds the isolated grassfarming communities together. A one-year subscription is $28.00. Nation also sells a variety of books about the grassfarming movement, including most of the ones listed in this section. The Stockman GrassFarmer, P.O. Box 2300, Ridgeland, MS 39158-2300. (800) 748-9808 Fax (601) 853-8087. http://www.stockmangrassfarmer.com/

Internet Links

http://www.eatwild.com is the website for *Why Grassfed Is Best!* and related books. The site features updated research about the benefits of grassfarming, plus a comprehensive directory of grassfarmers in the United States and Canada. You can also order books or correspond with the author.

http://www.stockmangrassfarmer.com/ This is the official website of *The Stockman GrassFarmer,* Allan Nation's monthly periodical. You can also order books about grassfarming through this site.

http://www.GrassFarmer.com This site is a comprehensive electronic information site on dairy grazing and grass-based farming systems . Visitors will be able to tour farming operations in the United States, Canada and New Zealand to see how graziers manage livestock on grass. This is also the web site of Cove Mt. Farm, a seasonal grass dairy operated by the American Farmland Trust to demonstrate the economic and environmental benefits of grassfarming.

http://factoryfarm.org/topic-humanhealth.html The focus of this website is to "eliminate factory farming in favor of a sustainable food production system which is healthful and humane, economically viable and environmentally sound."

http://www.ag.ohio-state.edu/`fair/ag/amazegrazeprev.html This site is an on-line publication about the science of grazing.

http://www.teleport.com/~jor This is the website for my previous book, *The Omega Diet*, a collaboration with Dr. Artemis P. Simopoulos about the benefits of eating a Mediterranean-style diet that has a balanced ratio of omega-3 and omega-6 fatty acids. Researching this book gave me the insights that led to *Why Grassfed is Best!*.

http://www.nhq.nrcs.usda.gov/BCS/graze/ nonfed.html   This USDA site has good information about the environmental benefits of grazing land, including a discussion on carbon sequestration, the phenomenon whereby pastureland absorbs carbon dioxide from the air and stores it in the soil as organic matter.

http://www.panix.com/~paleodiet/   A rich site devoted to an exploration of the Paleolithic diet. (A section titled "An Interview with Ward Nicholson" discusses major changes in the human evolutionary diet. Worth reading.)

http://www.nal.usda.gov/fnic/   This site contains information about the nutrient content of common foods, including individual fatty acids. Look for the USDA Nutrient Database for Standard Reference under the heading "Food Composition." The following table will help you understand the scientific notation for individual fatty acids. (Note: CLA is not included in this database.)

Name of fatty acid	Family	Scientific Notation
Linoleic (LA)	Omega-6	18:2
Alpha-linolenic (LNA)	Omega-3	18:3
Arachidonic (AA)	Omega-6	20:4
Eicosapentaenoic (EPA)	Omega-3	20:5
Docosahexaenoic (DHA)	Omega-3	22:6

http://www.nal.usda.gov/ag98/ is the website for AGRICOLA, an extensive government database of books and articles about agriculture.

http://www.ncbi.nlm.nih.gov/PubMed/ is the mother of all government medical databases. Go here to read abstracts of the medical studies cited in the Comments and Endnotes section of this book. If you want copies of the complete articles, you will need to go to a nearby medical library or have them delivered to you for a fee.

Comments and Endnotes

[1] Haapapuro, E. R., N. D. Barnard, *et al.* (1997). "Review—animal waste used as livestock feed: dangers to human health." <u>Prev Med</u> 26(5 Pt 1): 599-602. In 1994, Arkansas poultry producers fed 1,000 tons of poultry litter to cattle. The procedure is also common in some other geographic areas as a means of eliminating a portion of the 1.6 million tons of livestock wastes produced in the United States.

[2] Gillespie, J. R. (1997). <u>Modern Livestock and Poultry Production</u>. Albany, Delmar Publishers, p. 122.

[3] Rifkin, J. (1992). <u>Beyond Beef, The Rise and Fall of the Cattle Culture</u>. New York, Penguin, p. 12.

[4] Owens, F. N., D. S. Secrist, *et al.* (1998). "Acidosis in cattle: a review." <u>J Anim Sci</u> 76(1): 275-86. When ruminant animals become sick, whatever the cause, a standard remedy is to put them back on pasture to help them recover. According to Allan Nation, "Dr. Grass" has saved the lives of countless animals.

[5] <u>J. Animal Science</u>, 76:287-98, 1998 "Liver abscesses in feedlot cattle: a review."

[6] Roberts, J. L. (1982). "The prevalence and economic significance of liver disorders and contamination in grain-fed and grass-fed cattle." <u>Aust Vet J</u> 59(5): 129-32. According to a second article, (Nagaraja, T. G., M. L. Galyean, et al. (1998). "Nutrition and disease." <u>Vet Clin North Am Food Anim Pract</u> 14(2): 257-77.) "Mortality from digestive

diseases in feedlot cattle is second only to that from respiratory diseases. Acidosis and bloat are the major digestive disorders and are likely to continue because of ongoing attempts to improve the efficiency of beef production by feeding more grain and less roughage." Cattle raised on pasture-intensive farms are not subjected to this inhumane treatment.

[7] Grady, D. (1999). A Move to Limit Antibiotic Use in Animal Feed. The New York Times. New York: National Desk.

[8] Glynn, M. K., C. Bopp, et al. (1998). "Emergence of multidrug-resistant Salmonella enterica serotype typhimurium DT104 infections in the United States." N Engl J Med 338(19): 1333-8.

[9] Chou, T. (1999). "Emerging infectious diseases and pathogens." Nurs Clin North Am 34(2): 427-42.

[10] Epstein, S. S. (1996). "Unlabeled milk from cows treated with biosynthetic growth hormones: a case of regulatory abdication." Int J Health Serv 26(1): 173-85. According to this article:"Levels of insulin-like growth factor-1 (IGF-1) are substantially elevated and more bioactive in the milk of cows hyperstimulated with the biosynthetic bovine growth hormones rBGH. IGF-1 is absorbed from the gastrointestinal tract, as evidenced by marked growth-promoting effects even in short-term tests in mature rats, and absorption is likely to be still higher in infants."

[11] Fukumoto, G. K., Y.S. Kim, D. Oduda, H. Ako (1995). "Chemical composition and shear force requirement of loin eye muscle of young, forage-

fed steers." <u>Research Extension Series 161</u>: 1-5. The information on fat content comes from other sources as well, including a study by the University of Wisconsin (Madison) Meat Science Department of grassfed cattle raised on the Cattleana Ranch in Omro, Wisconsin.

[12] Maron, D. J., J. M. Fair, et al. (1991). "Saturated fat intake and insulin resistance in men with coronary artery disease. The Stanford Coronary Risk Intervention Project Investigators and Staff." <u>Circulation</u> **84**(5): 2020-7.

[13] *Ibid.*

[14] Denke, M. A. (1994). "Role of beef and beef tallow, an enriched source of stearic acid, in a cholesterol-lowering diet." <u>Am J Clin Nutr, 60</u>(6 Suppl), 1044S-1049S.

[15]The calorie data comes from the analysis of Cattleana pasture-finished beef noted in endnote 11.

[16] Fukumoto, G. K., Y.S. Kim, D. Oduda, H. Ako (1995). "Chemical composition and shear force requirement of loin eye muscle of young, forage-fed steers." <u>Research Extension Series 161</u>: 1-5. Koizumi, I., Y. Suzuki, et al. (1991). "Studies on the fatty acid composition of intramuscular lipids of cattle, pigs and birds." <u>J Nutr Sci Vitaminol (Tokyo)</u> **37**(6): 545-54.

[17]For a readable, comprehensive discussion of the many roles that omega-3 fatty acids play in human health, read my previous book, *The Omega Diet*, a collaboration with Dr. Artemis P. Simopoulos. (1999. HarperCollins)   (You can also order this book at my

website, www.eatwild.com)

[18] Hibbeln, J. R. and N. Salem (1995). "Dietary polyunsaturated fatty acids and depression: when cholesterol does not satisfy." American Journal of Clinical Nutrition 62: 1-9. According to this article, "Epidemiological studies in various countries and in the United States in the last century suggest that decreased n-3 [omega-3] fatty acid consumption correlates with increasing rates of depression. This is consistent with a well-established positive correlation between depression and coronary artery disease. Long-chain n-3 polyunsaturate deficiency may also contribute to depressive symptoms in alcoholism, multiple sclerosis, and postpartum depression. We postulate that adequate long-chain polyunsaturated fatty acids, particularly docasahexaenoic acid, may reduce the development of depression just as n-3 polyunsaturated fatty acids may reduce coronary artery disease."

[19] Schaefer, E. J. "Decreased Plasma Phosphatidyl-choline Docosohexaenoic Acid Content in Dementia." Unpublished abstract. In this study of 51 elderly Dutch men, men who had diets rich in omega-3s (from fish) were least likely to be senile.

[20] Stoll, A. L., W. E. Severus, et al. (1999). "Omega 3 fatty acids in bipolar disorder: a preliminary double-blind, placebo-controlled trial." Arch Gen Psychiatry 56(5): 407-12. According to this study, "Omega-3 fatty acids were well tolerated and improved the short-term course of illness in this preliminary study of patients with bipolar disorder." Studies are also underway to see if omega-3 supplements can improve the course of Alzheimer's disease, depression, ADHD and schizophrenia.

[21] Leaf, A. and J. X. Kang (1996). "Antiarrhythmic Effects of Polyunsaturated Fatty Acids." Circulation **94**(7): 1774-80.

[22] Hu, F. B., M. J. Stampfer, et al. (1999). "Dietary intake of alpha-linolenic acid and risk of fatal ischemic heart disease among women." Am J Clin Nutr **69**(5): 890-7. In this 1999 study, women with the lowest levels of omega-3s in their diet were twice as likely to die of a heart attack as those with the highest levels. (The type of omega-3 that was measured, LNA, is precisely the type most abundant in grassfed animals.)

[23] Dolecek, T. A. and G. Grandits (1991). "Dietary Polyunsaturated Fatty Acids and Mortality in the Multiple Risk Factor Intervention Trial (MRFIT)." World Rev Nutr Diet **66**: 205-16.) In this study of 12,866 American men, one of the largest dietary surveys ever conducted, men whose diets were deficient in omega-3 fatty acids had a significantly increased risk of dying from cancer. This survey also determined that a diet rich in omega-3s may reduce the risk of cancer. Those men with the greatest amount of omega-3s and the least amount of a competing fat called omega-6 fatty acids (which is found in grains) had a 33 percent lower risk of dying from cancer.

[24] Bougnoux, P., V. Chajes, et al. (1994). "Role of 18:3n-3 Content of Breast Adipose Tissue: A Host Indicator of Subsequent Metastasis in Breast Cancer?" Br. J. Cancer **70**: 330-4.

[25] de Lorgeril, M., P. Salen, et al. (1998). "Mediterranean dietary pattern in a randomized trial: prolonged survival and possible reduced cancer rate."

113

Arch Intern Med **158**(11): 1181-
This diet, called "The Lyon Heart Diet," is the model diet for the program described in my previous book, *The Omega Diet.*

[26] Dolecek, T. A. and G. Grandits (1991). "Dietary Polyunsaturated Fatty Acids and Mortality in the Multiple Risk Factor Intervention Trial (MRFIT)." World Rev Nutr Diet **66**: 205-16.)

[27] Duckett, S. K., D. G. Wagner, et al. (1993). "Effects of time on feed on beef nutrient composition." J Anim Sci **71**(8): 2079-88.

[28] Simopoulos and Robinson, The Omega Diet, HarperCollins, 1999. This book explores the importance of having a balanced ratio of omega-6 and omega-3 fatty acids in detail.

[29] The data on the nutrient composition of the grain-fed bison comes from the following study: Marchello, M. J., et al (1998). "Nutrient Composition of Bison Fed Concentrate Diets." Journal of Food Composition and Analysis **11**: 231-9. The contrasting data on grassfed bison comes from an unpublished nutritional analysis by Marchello of 31 grassfed bison raised by Texas grassfarmers.

[30] Hebeisen, D. F., F. Hoeflin, et al. (1993). "Increased concentrations of omega-3 fatty acids in milk and platelet rich plasma of grass-fed cows." Int J Vitam Nutr Res **63**(3): 229-33. From the article: ". . . we tested the hypothesis that platelet rich plasma and milk from cows feeding exclusively on green grass contains more omega-3 fatty acids than milk from cows fed conserved grass. . . Half a liter of milk from grass-fed cows provides approximately 191 mg 18:3 [alpha-linolenic, an omega-3

fatty acid] and 14 mg 20:5 [eicosapentanoic or EPA, a long-chain omega-3 fatty acid.] In this regard milk from grass fed cows may be nutritionally superior . . ."

[31] Dhiman, T. R., G. R. Anand, et al. (1999). "Conjugated linoleic acid content of milk from cows fed different diets." J Dairy Sci **82**(10): 2146-2156.

[32] *Ibid.* Omega-3 fatty acids also have anti-tumor activity, but only when fed at a higher percentage of the diet. CLA is effective in very small doses.

[33] Ip, C., J. A. Scimeca, et al. (1994). "Conjugated linoleic acid. A powerful anti-carcinogen from animal fat sources." p. 1053. Cancer **74**(3 Suppl): 1050-4.

[34] Knekt, P., *et al.* (1996). Intake of dairy products and the risk of breast cancer. Br. J. Cancer, **73**, 687-691.

[35] Garland, Cedric F. "The assessment of the epidemiological evidence on the role of dairy foods and dairy food components of colon cancer risk." Department of Family and Preventive Medicine School of Medicine, University of California, San Diego. Unfortunately, none of the dietary surveys has determined whether the milk came from grass-fed or grain-fed cows, which means they cannot give a true indication of the benefits of CLA.

[36] M. Pariza *et al.*, "Mechanism of body fat reduction by conjugated linoleic acid feeding in the mouse." FASEB J. 11.3 (1997): A580.

[37] The study was conducted by Erling Thom, Ph.D., from Medstat Research Ltd., in Lillestrom, Norway,

and was presented at the 1997 Federation for Applied Science and Experimental Biology (FASEB) national meeting in New Orleans.

[38] Lowery, L. M. *et al.* (1998). "Conjugated linoleic acid enhances muscle size and strength gains in novice bodybuilders." <u>Medicine and Science in Sports and Exercise</u> **30**(5): S182. This article concluded that "CLA acts as a mild anabolic agent in novice male bodybuilders."

[39] Parodi, P.W. "Symposium: A bold new look at milk fat." (1999) J Dairy Sci 82:1339-1349. There are different types of conjugated linoleic acid. The type believed to be most biologically active has double bonds in the 9th and 11th position. Virtually all of the CLA in ruminants is of this type. Only 40 percent of commercial preparations has this optimal configuration.

[40] Dhiman, T. R., G. R. Anand, et al. (1999). "Conjugated linoleic acid content of milk from cows fed different diets." <u>J Dairy Sci</u> **82**(10): 2146-56.

[41] This finding is from an unpublished study conducted by Dr. Tikal Dhiman.

[42] Ip, C. *op cit.*

[43] Personal communication.

[44] Dhiman, *op cit.* Interestingly, when the pasture was cut and then fed to the animals as hay, the cows produced far less CLA, even though it was the very same grass. The fat that the animals use to produce CLA (in this case, LNA) is destroyed during the wilting, drying process. For maximum CLA, animals need to be grazing living pasture.

[45] van Poppel, G. (1996). "Epidemiological evidence for beta-carotene in prevention of cancer and cardiovascular disease." Eur J Clin Nutr **50 Suppl 3**: S57-61.

[46] Nader, Glenn and Steve Blank. "Thinking through the process: grassfed beef." University of California Sustainable Agriculture Research and Education Program.

[47] Herriott, D. E., D. D. Hancock, et al. (1998). "Association of herd management factors with colonization of dairy cattle by Shiga toxin-positive Escherichia coli O157." J Food Prot **61**(7): 802-7.

[48] Diez-Gonzalez, F., T. R. Callaway, et al. (1998). "Grain feeding and the dissemination of acid-resistant Escherichia coli from cattle" Science **281**(5383): 1666-8. In this article, the researchers commented "Grain-feeding is a practice that promotes the production and efficiency of cattle production, and it is unlikely that American cattle will ever be fed diets consisting of hay." We are fortunate that pioneering grassfarmers are proving them wrong.

[49] Lenhart, S. W. and S. A. Olenchock (1984). "Sources of respiratory insult in the poultry processing industry." Am J Ind Med **6**(2): 89-96.

[50] The plight of chicken factory workers was explored by 60 Minutes reporters in a program first aired on December 19th, 1999.

[51] Donoghue, D. J., H. Hairston, et al. (1997). "Modeling drug residue uptake by eggs: yolks contain ampicillin residues even after drug withdrawal and

nondetectability in the plasma." <u>Poult Sci</u> **76**(3): 458-62. The conclusion of this study was that: "drug residues are contained in eggs laid a number of days after drug withdrawal."

[52] Papadopoulou, C., D. Dimitriou, et al. (1997). "Bacterial strains isolated from eggs and their resistance to currently used antibiotics: is there a health hazard for consumers?" <u>Comp Immunol Microbiol Infect Dis</u> **20**(1): 35-40.

[53] Simopoulos, A. P. (1989). "n-3 Fatty acids in eggs from range-fed Greek chickens." <u>The New England Journal of Medicine</u>: 1412.

54 Davis, K. (1996). <u>Prisoned Chickens, Poisoned Eggs</u>. Summertown Tennesse, Book Publishing Company.

[55] Kocamis, H., Y. N. Yeni, et al. (1999). "Postnatal growth of broilers in response to in ovo administration of chicken growth hormone." <u>Poult Sci</u> **78**(8): 1219-26.

[56] The SARE grant was obtained by Barbara Gorski and was used to analyze eggs and chickens from her Double G Farm and two neighboring farms, Forks Farm and the Lone Pine Farm.

[57] Jiang, Z. e. a. (1993). "Consumption of n-3 [omega-3] polyunsaturated fatty acid-enriched eggs and changes in plasma lipids in human subjects." <u>Nutrition</u> **9**: 513-518.
Note: The amount of omega-3 fatty acids in eggs from pastured poultry varies from farm to farm according to the type of greens found in the field and the amount of omega-3s in the chickens' supplemental grains. For the highest omega-3

content, look for farmers that add flaxseeds, fishmeal, millet, seaweed, or algae to their grain.

[58] For more of Tyson's view of free-range chickens, visit their corporate website: http://www.tyson.com./chicken/faq/freerange.asp

[59] Eaton, S. B., S. B. I. Eaton, et al. (1996). "An Evolutionary Perspective Enhances Understanding of Human Nutritional Requirements." American Institute of Nutrition **126**: 1732-40. Boyd Eaton has devoted his career to understanding the links between nutrition and evolution.

[60] Crawford, M. A. (1968). "Fatty-Acid ratios in free-living and domestic animals." The Lancet **1**: 1329-33.

[61] Sponheimer, M. and J. A. Lee-Thorp (1999). "Isotopic evidence for the diet of an early hominid, Australopithecus africanus ." Science **283**(5400): 368-70. In this study, researchers analyzed the isotopes (atoms of the same element that have a different number of neutrons) of the tooth enamel of early humans and found that from 25 to 50 percent of their diet consisted of either grass, or far more likely, grass-eating animals. Some people theorize that we owe our large brains to this bounty of wild game and seafood, food that supplied high quality protein and omega-3 fatty acids, which are essential for the development of the brain. [For more information about this theory, see Eaton, S. B., Konner, M.J., Shostak, M. (1996)." An evolutionary perspective enhances understanding of human nutritional requirements." J. Nutr., 126, 1732-1740.] Had we remained plant eaters, we might not have developed our remarkable mental abilities.

[60] Eaton, B. and M. Konner (1985). "Paleolithic Nutrition: A Consideration of Its Nature and Current Implications." <u>The New England Journal of Medicine</u> **312**(5): 283-9.

[62] Anna Curtenius Roosevelt, "Population, Health, and the Evolution of Subsistence: Conclusions from the Conference," in Paleopathology and the Origins of Agriculture, eds. Mark N. Cohen and George J. Armelagos (Orlando, FLA.: Academic Press, 1984.) pp. 572-574.

[63] Haviland, W. A. (1994). <u>Anthropology</u>. Fort Worth, Harcourt Brace College Publishers. P. 244.

[64] <u>Beef Cattle Science</u>, 5th Edition, 1976. M.E. Ensminger, Publisher. Publisher, The Interstate. p. 1249.

[65] Rifkin, J. (1992). <u>Beyond Beef, The Rise and Fall of the Cattle Culture</u>. New York, Penguin., p. 161

[66] *Ibid.* p. 13

[67] Barboza, D. (1999). Biotech Companies Take on Critics of Gene-Altered Food. <u>The New York Times</u>. November 12: A1, A18.

[68] Losey, J. E., L. S. Rayor, *et al.* (1999). "Transgenic pollen harms monarch larvae [letter]" <u>Nature</u> **399**(6733): 214.

[69] Ewen, S. W. and A. Pusztai (1999). "Effect of diets containing genetically modified potatoes expressing Galanthus nivalis lectin on rat small intestine [letter]" <u>Lancet</u> **354**(9187): 1353-4.

120

[70] Rifkin, J. *op. cit.*

[71] Haapapuro, E. R., N. D. Barnard, *et al.* (1997). "Review—animal waste used as livestock feed: dangers to human health." <u>Prev Med</u> **26**(5 Pt 1): 599-602.

[72] Murray, L. (1999). Dead Zone Hit Record in the Gulf. <u>The New York Times</u>. New York: D4.

[73] You can read about the techniques and philosophy involved in raising animals on rich pasture in Salatin's book, *Salad Bar Beef*, Ó 1995, published by Polyface, Inc., Swope Virginia. ISBN 0-9638109-1-X.

[74] Collins, Scott L., *et al.* (1998.) "Modulation of Diversity by Grazing and Mowing in Native Tallgrass Prairie." Science 280:745-747. Since learning about this study, the Nature Conservancy, an environmental group devoted to preserving wilderness, has invited several grassfarmers to graze their animals on their protected land.

[75] Nation, A. (1995). <u>Quality Pasture, How to create it, manage it, and profit from it</u>. Jackson, Green Park Press. p. 8

[76] Hardin, Ben. "Predicting Tenderness in Beefsteaks" Agricultural Research, November 1999. [Note: Agricultural Research is a USDA publication.]

Note: You can also purchase books online at
www.eatwild.com.

ORDER FORM
Why Grassfed is Best!
by Jo Robinson

Single copy	$7.50
2-5 copies	$7.00 each
6-10 copies	$6.50 each
11-15 copies	$6.00 each

(Call for larger orders, 206-463-4156)

Number of Books _____

Cost of books _____
Shipping and handling* _____
Tax (Washington residents _____
Only)
Total Cost _____

Ship to _____
_____
_____
_____

Phone _____
e-mail _____

Make check payable to Vashon Island Press and send to Vashon
Island Press, 29428 129th Ave S.W., Vashon WA 98070-8824.

*Add $2.50 shipping and handling for first class delivery on single
copies, $5.00 for 2-5 copies, $7.00 for 6-10 copies. $9.00 for 11-
15 copies. Call for bulk rate and shipping costs on larger orders.
(206) 463-4156 (9am - 5pm PST.)

** If ordering within Washington State, add 8.5 percent tax.

ORDER FORM

The Omega Diet
by Simopoulos and Robinson

Single copy $14.00
(Call for multiple copies, 206-463-4156)

Cost of book   _____
Shipping and handling*   _____
Tax (Washington residents   _____
Only)
                        Total Cost   _____

Ship to   _____

                _____

                _____

                _____

Phone   _____
e-mail _____

Make check payable to Vashon Island Press and send to Vashon
Island Press, 29428 129th Ave S.W., Vashon WA 98070-8824.
Questions? Call for bulk rate and shipping costs on larger
orders. (206) 463-4156 (9am - 5pm PST.)

*Add $3.50 shipping and handling for first class delivery, $2.50
for book rate.

** If ordering within Washington State, add 8.5 percent tax.

Index